D1271961

BC

RC 460 .B53 1953
Bingham, June, 1919-
  The inside story : psychiatry and
everyday life

RC
763
3

The Inside Story

The Inside Story

PSYCHIATRY AND EVERYDAY LIFE

◇◇

Compiled under the direction of

FRITZ REDLICH, M.D.

Chairman, Department of Psychiatry
Yale University School of Medicine

Text written by

JUNE BINGHAM

With the collaboration of

JACOB LEVINE, PH.D.

Chief Clinical Psychologist
Veterans Administration Hospital, Newington, Conn.

NEW YORK: ALFRED·A·KNOPF: 1953

RC
460
.B53
1953

L. C. catalog card number: 52–12211

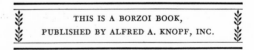

THIS IS A BORZOI BOOK,
PUBLISHED BY ALFRED A. KNOPF, INC.

Copyright 1953 by June R. Bingham. All rights reserved. No part of this book may be reproduced in any form without permission in writing from the publisher, except by a reviewer who may quote brief passages and reproduce not more than three illustrations in a review to be printed in a magazine or newspaper. Manufactured in the United States of America. Published simultaneously in Canada by McClelland & Stewart Limited.

Published May 18, 1953
Second Printing, September 1953

TO

E.A.R. *and* J.B.B.

Even a fool, when he holdeth

his peace, is counted wise.

PROV. XVII, 28

Acknowledgments

WE ARE HAPPY to express our appreciation to the artists whose ability to condense into a few pencil strokes the most complex human emotions has won our admiration:

Charles Addams	Mary Gibson
Peter Arno	Walter Goldstein
Elmer Atkins	Sid Gordin (Sivic)
John Bailey	Ray Helle
George Baker	Tom Henderson
Berenstain	Sydney Hoff
Henry Boltinoff	Tom Hudson
Irving Caplan	Dave Huffine
Claude	Foster Humfreville
Sam Cobean	Hank Ketcham
Lester Colin	Bill King
Bruce Currie	Kovarsky
Chon Day	David Langdon
Abner Dean	Cissie Liebschutz
Dana Fradon	Gustav Lundberg
Leo Garel	Harry Mace

[ix

ACKNOWLEDGMENTS

Jack Markow	Salo Roth
Charles E. Martin	O. Soglow
Frank Modell	Howard Sparber
Ed Nofziger	Steinberg
Gladys Parker	Scott Taber
Virgil Partch	James Thurber
Gardner Rea	Linda Walter
Mischa Richter	Webster
Irving Roir	Al Wiseman
Carl Rose	Peter Wyma

Grateful acknowledgment is made to the following individuals, publications, and corporations for permission to reprint the cartoons in this book: George Baker; Abner Dean; *The American Legion Magazine*; *Argosy*; *Collier's*; *Medical Economics*; The Newspaper *PM*; *New York Herald Tribune*; *The New Yorker Magazine, Inc.*; *Park East, The Magazine of New York*; Proprietors of *Punch*; *Saturday Evening Post*; *Saturday Review of Literature*; *This Week Magazine*; *True, The Man's Magazine*; The Associated Newspapers, Inc.; Fawcett Publications, Inc.; King Features Syndicate, Inc.; Simon and Schuster; United Newspapers Magazine Corporation.

We wish to take this opportunity to extend our thanks to Dr. Theodore Sohler for his invaluable suggestions and

ACKNOWLEDGMENTS

advice during the early crucial stages of plotting out the book, and last but not least to Miss Lois Young for her indefatigable typing and retyping and the many other forms of assistance that she has given.

Contents

The Psychiatrist's Prescription

FRITZ REDLICH, M. D.
333 CEDAR STREET
NEW HAVEN, CONNECTICUT

℞

1. Look at the cartoons and enjoy them as much as you can.

2. Read the text when you feel like it, allowing it to combine with the cartoons in arousing your own memories and feelings.

3. Let some time pass.

4. Look at the cartoons again. You may know more about them and yourself and enjoy them even more.

S. For anyone interested in human problems.

Fritz Redlich MD

The Inside Story

The Layman's Preface

◇◇

All the world is queer save thee and me, and even thou art a little queer.

ROBERT OWEN

THE COLLABORATION of a psychiatrist, a psychologist, and a skeptical layman has turned out to be like one of those stage-horses in which the front goes one way and the rear

the other, and eventually the whole horse has to sit down and take its bearings.

Dr. Redlich would look at a cartoon and see a hundred different unconscious emotions involved in its appeal. I would look at it and see none. Dr. Levine would then look at me and wonder why I didn't see any. (According to the specialists, there are unconscious reasons why we are not amused as well as why we are; it was apparently no accident that Queen Victoria was "not amused" by sex.) Dr. Redlich and Dr. Levine would then look at each other and conjecture whether this negative reaction of mine was typical of most laymen and therefore of significance for the book, or whether I was simply a potential patient for the Yale Psychiatric Clinic, which, conveniently for them, but uncomfortably for me, adjoined the office where we worked.

Needless to say, at about that stage we'd start all over again. Then this in itself would cause complications. For after one has looked at the same batch of cartoons enough times, one forgets whether one ever did think they were funny. The only sure thing is that they aren't very funny any more.

After the initial choice of cartoons—out of the doctors' collection of some thirty thousand—came the tangles with editors of magazines. Some editors considered our request to use their cartoons as a compliment; others felt rather firmly the opposite. Among the editors who were reluctant to grant permission were a few who attached the condition that there be no psychoanalyzing of cartoons. Their theory seemed to be that if artists became aware of what it was they had been doing all these years they might never be able to do it again.

Another editor wrote that we could have some but not all the cartoons we had requested. His magazine had a long-established rule that its cartoons could not make up more than a certain percentage of the total in any outside collection. What was our total going to be? Of this we had not the slightest idea. For one thing, we each kept turning up new cartoons we insisted were far too good to leave out. For another, as it turned out later, we had each been surreptitiously throwing out cartoons selected by the other two. Nothing daunted, we decided this was a problem of prime urgency. Since the two doctors were in Connecticut and I was in New York and there was no fund for long-distance telephone calls, the result was that the long-suffering editor of this magazine received letters from two different states asking for two different sets of cartoons for the identical book whose cartoon total was given as two separate figures (and he was lucky there weren't three). At this point the sitting-down stage-horse looked as if it would never get up again.

But agreeing on the cartoons was child's play compared with selecting ideas for the text. One of us wanted to include everything psychiatry had discovered since Freud was a babe in arms; another of us was afraid to do more than skim the psychiatric cream, so to speak, in order to avoid both the dull fundamental skim-milk and also the high-smelling, though to some people delicious, cheeses that abound in this field. Finally we compromised on limiting the book to those psychiatric concepts which can be useful in everyday life, and leaving out those which are useful primarily in doctors' offices.

But among those concepts which are useful in everyday life—indeed, perhaps the ones that are most useful of all—are some to which people often respond by saying "rubbish" or "well, that may be true of some people but certainly not of me." Our problem was how, without being boringly clinical, to convince people of facts about themselves which they didn't know, didn't want to know, and didn't want to know that they didn't want to know.

When you come right down to it, who but a psychiatrist * *would* want to know that a substantial part of each of us is beyond conscious control, and that our feelings and our actions, like the limbs of a puppet, are liable to be yanked by invisible strings?

In attempting to convey these concepts, we decided to let the cartoons work on the reader and the reader work on himself. When he responds to a cartoon either by a laugh or a frown or a glassy stare of noncomprehension, he will be indicating that something within himself has been stirred by the subject matter of that cartoon. What might this be? Sometimes he will be able to spot it right away; sometimes,

---

* From here on we will refer only to psychiatrists, although what is said will usually also apply to their professional colleagues, the clinical psychologists, and the psychiatric social workers.

not for a while; sometimes, never. But all three kinds of reaction on his part can be significant.

Of course, the cartoon itself might be so poor that its point doesn't get across. But since all cartoons in this book have been agreed on by the three of us—with our divergent points of view—as being at least somewhat amusing, we feel it safe to say that the reader's varying reactions will have more to do with what's inherent in him than what's inherent in the cartoons.

Many of the cartoons are lifted from a collection already shown to hundreds of mental patients and normal "controls" at the Yale School of Medicine, in a test that uses the patient's reactions to the cartoons to determine what form of mental illness, if any, he is suffering from. The results of this Mirth Response Test have, so far, jibed remarkably with the results of such other diagnostic tests as the Rorschach and Thematic Apperception tests.* Most of the time when patients laughed uncontrollably (sometimes they had to be given sedatives) at a cartoon, or when they were unable to see why it was supposed to be funny, its subject matter was later found to touch on one of their key areas of emotional disturbance.

One woman became extremely agitated after being shown a Peter Arno cartoon of a swimming contest in which three muscular, plain-looking girl swimmers are looking jealously at a slim, curvaceous one whom the male judges too are admiring. Months later, psychoanalysis of this patient, whose father had never shown her any affection

---

* See Glossary for definitions of technical terms. When these terms have different meanings for laymen and professionals, both are given.

or approval, uncovered her deep-seated terror that she would never be wholly a woman and that, do what she might, she could never claim the love of a man.

And seriously ill (schizophrenic) patients were never able to see any point whatsoever in the famous Addams skiing cartoon of the man on the slope looking back at the marks of skis, one on either side of a big tree. "But why not?" asked these patients who live so much in a magic world of their own: "Why shouldn't a person have one leg able to go on one side of a tree while the other leg goes on the other? Why, if you knew what I know . . ."

After describing several more cases like these, the two doctors offered, as a special favor, to run the Mirth Response Test off on me. I busied myself mightily with my papers and said I really thought we shouldn't waste the time. Didn't they think that this cartoon was a particularly apt one for the second chapter? *

The advantage the reader of this book has over anyone being given the Mirth Response Test, besides not having a doctor breathing down his neck, is that he can combine in himself the role of guinea pig and scientist. He can first react spontaneously (unconsciously) to the cartoons and then later, if he feels like it, can consciously ponder the significance of this reaction.

Adjoining each cartoon appears a running text on the same general subject which the reader can use as a springboard into the pool of his own memories and associations. Or, if he prefers, he can look at the cartoons first and try to guess what the psychiatrists have to say about their subject

---

* It is possible to fool some of the psychiatrists some of the time. . . .

8]

matter. Or he can first read the rather boring but essential next chapter, which describes why human beings repress

certain feelings and why these feelings explode into laughter—and other things. Or he can bone up on the text first and then spring the cartoons on his friends. Or he can *not* read the book, and give it to his friends—just as long as he pays for it, we really don't mind.

Actually, the three of us are a form of creature difficult to visualize: a crusader with his tongue in his cheek. So deeply do we feel that the discoveries of modern dynamic

[9

psychology are important to people, both for their under-standing of themselves and their children and for the living of richer, happier, and more creative lives, that we have to laugh about it; otherwise we'd cry in our frustration at the slowness with which these concepts are currently being accepted.

One is often told that he who laughs last, laughs best. In this instance, we have laughed first. Without trying to be unduly noble, may we say that it would give us the greatest satisfaction if the reader who laughs after us laughs best of all.

(((I)))

The Key to Laughter:
Repression

◇◇◇

One inch of joy surmounts of grief a span,
Because to laugh is proper to the man.

RABELAIS

IF A PSYCHIATRIST went to a primitive island (as, like other people, he may dream of doing), and if he showed the natives a glowing flashlight, the chances are that they would either kill or worship him. His problem would be to convince them of the fantastic fact that electricity exists.

Psychiatrists have somewhat the same problem here at home (without the island benefits) when they try to convince people that another fantastic force of nature exists, as ever-restless as electricity, as impossible to witness except through its results, and as capable of being put to both good and evil use. This force, which appears, as far as we know, only in human beings, was discovered by Freud and named repression. It has two elements: one the repressed *material*, the urges and experiences that are kept unconscious; and

[11

the other the repressing *power*, which is also unconscious and which serves, like a policeman or censor, both when we are asleep and awake, to keep the repressed material from emerging into our awareness.

When we speak of unconsciousness, we may mean one of a variety of things. We may mean ignorance, as in being

unconscious of what is going on around us; or partial unconsciousness, as in sleep; or total unconsciousness, as in being knocked out. But generally, when we refer to some feeling as being unconscious, we mean that we were temporarily not conscious of it; we do not mean that never, as long as we live, will we become conscious of it. Yet the likelihood of such permanent unconsciousness is precisely what repression does mean. If once we felt an experience to be so threatening that we literally couldn't bear to think about it, we may have thrust it so far beyond the reach of our conscious thinking that even if we were confronted with evidence of its having occurred we would still sincerely deny that it had.

Besides the likelihood of permanent unconsciousness which distinguishes a repressed memory from a plain forgotten one, there is also a restless (dynamic) quality to the repressed one which is absent from the other. An experience that is simply forgotten drops away like a pebble in a pond. There it lies peacefully on the bottom, more or less within sight. No matter how often it is joined by similar pebbles it can usually, in time, be fished up again by the conscious self. But a repressed experience is like a buoy being held beneath the surface by a tangled anchor-chain. The buoy strives constantly to rise, the chain constantly holds it down. The whole thing is too slippery for the grappling-hook of the conscious self, by its own efforts, to catch hold of and release. And the greater the number of similar submerged buoys and chains to join and perhaps become further entangled with it, the greater the degree of unconscious tension.

This continuing unconscious tension, which exists to some extent in all human beings, is sometimes constructively channeled (sublimated) and at other times causes irrational feelings or acts that may be harmful to ourselves or to others.

By and large, when any of us feels or does something that doesn't make sense or seems out of character, it is a sign that old repressions are at work. Here was part of Freud's discovery: that the feelings and acts which we don't understand do make sense, after their fashion. Theirs is a pattern of operation which is different from that of the conscious mind, but which becomes understandable and even predictable by the conscious mind if studied in terms of emotion rather than of logic. This pattern is composed of a number of unconscious tendencies. These may be in

harmony or in conflict with one another and also with the rational dictates of consciousness. Several of them may be mobilized within the process of repression, and at such times we cannot possibly spot their action. But when they operate independently of repression, they may be close enough to consciousness for us to catch sight of them whisking through our daytime lives and our nighttime dreams. In brief, these unconscious tendencies are the following:

1. *Tit-for-tat.* You hurt me so I hurt you. If I, for example, break something of yours, unconsciously my first reaction will probably be fear that you will break something of mine; and unconsciously your first reaction probably will be to break something of mine (or me). It may take a moment before

The King's Library

I can reasonably tell myself: "Don't just stand there (as if prepared to defend myself against you), but do something,"

either in terms of picking up the pieces or attempting to replace the broken object.

2. *Belief in symbols.* Mysterious events, often of the tit-for-tat variety, which our conscious self assures us are illogical, none the less hold emotional power over us. Many normal

people, not otherwise superstitious, will, after boasting of some good luck, "touch wood" to fend off an appropriate (tit-for-tat) punishment. Or some omen, like the sun shining on our wedding day, will affect us deeply despite our conscious knowledge that the appearance of the sun has more to do with weather conditions than with marital conditions.

3. *Imperviousness to time.* In the deeply unconscious part of us, as in dreams, events that in reality follow after one another can exist simultaneously. We can feel like a baby

and a child and an adult all at the same time. Some adults, for example, still respond to the permitted touching by their mate with the same shame and guilt that once they were

taught to associate with forbidden, childish touching of themselves. Although consciously they know perfectly well that they are no longer children, this passage of time holds no validity in the deep part of the unconscious where, in this instance, the repressed, unresolved conflict about sex was still tugging at the tangled anchor-chain.

4. *Inconsistency.* Unconsciously we can hold opposite feelings at the same time. As in dreams, we may go after what we

want despite the disapproval of someone we love, and yet more than anything in the world, at that very moment, we may crave the approval of that person. Consciously our feelings can vary; but unconsciously they can be *both* ways at once.

5. *Imperviousness to reason.* Deep in the unconscious part of us we apparently do not learn by way of reasoning through to new conclusions. Since words are necessary to reasoning and since verbalization is largely the function of the so-called higher centers of the brain, which are responsible for consciousness or near-consciousness, it is not surprising that logical decision is also largely limited to these centers. Sometimes, because of this imperviousness to reason, we can be confronted with the most self-evident facts and yet still remain unconvinced.

6. *Momentum.* Once started in some emotional direction, we often can't reverse ourselves. When a prejudice, say, becomes deeply ingrained, we tend to continue it throughout life. Even when challenged, we may say: "I logically agree that I am wrong, but I can't help feeling the way I do; it's the way I'm made, I guess." But what has "made" us that way? Not nature, for babies have been tested and found to be without prejudice except against loud noises, bright lights,

and the feeling of falling. It must have been some past experience that made us start out in that direction, and now

our unconscious momentum still keeps us going down that
same old single track.

7. *Seeking pleasure.* Even consciously, sometimes, we have
the feeling that we would like to eat up all the food in the

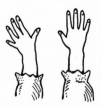

world, wear all the clothes, love and be loved by everyone,
and be able to flail out with wild abandon at whatever gets

in our way. And unconsciously such primitive insatiability continues to underlie even our moments of great conscious satisfaction. It is all too easy to arouse discontent in others or to become aware of it in ourselves; even when we determinedly count our blessings and recognize how lucky we are, we may not *feel* lucky or satisfied.

8. *Avoiding pain.* The greatest happiness in the world has been described as relief from pain. Whether this is true or not, we do seem to be unconsciously prepared to go to almost any lengths to avoid suffering. But, perhaps because we are

limited by the other unconscious tendencies, such as imperviousness to time and reason, we don't always succeed. Sometimes in our blind hurry to avoid one kind of suffering we promptly involve ourselves in another. Many of the painful symptoms of mental illness fall into this latter category.

In addition to these eight, there are other complicated unconscious tendencies whereby any of us can "sleep on" a decision and arrive at an answer, whereby artists and thinkers can "come up with" their creations, and whereby devotion to another person or to an ideal can become even more immediate than the fundamental instinct of self-preservation. So much more deeply unconscious than the other eight tendencies do these particular ones seem to be—whether they are connected with repression or not—that psychiatry, at the present state of knowledge, can discern only their results, not their component parts. And even if some day psychiatry does discover how they work, their operation will probably turn out to be as irrevocably unconscious, from the point of view of their individual host, as is the operation of his repressing *power* or unconscious policeman. Actually, the different degrees of consciousness and unconsciousness within the human mind are, as Dr. Paul Schilder has pointed out, similar to a solar system, with a high degree of light in the center, darkness at the periphery, and varying gradations in between.

Moreover, all degrees of light and darkness appear, to some extent, to fulfill a useful function. One function of consciousness is to enable us to cope with reality. Yet, if we were conscious at all times of everything in and around us, we could probably never concentrate effectively on any one thing. Some activities, like playing the piano, demand many different kinds of unconsciousness. We must not only learn to ignore current distractions and to forget the various steps in the past by which we have acquired our skill, but we must also shed some of our awareness of ourselves in order to develop that form of unselfconsciousness which is called mastery.

But if it's useful to have some of our repressed material remain unconscious, why not let all of it remain unconscious? Why not let sleeping dogs lie?

Because, for one thing, repressions are not sleeping dogs. They may play possum, but they are wide awake and ready to spring into action whenever some event in our life stirs them up. Nor can the kind of repression that this book de-

scribes * be kept from showing up in everyday life, in the ordinary course of growing up, going to school, getting married, holding down a job, becoming a parent, having loved ones die and ourselves grow old. For another thing, since these particular common repressions usually date from childhood, when the personality was still unmolded and unsure, there is no reason why as mature persons, or even as adolescents, we need any longer shrink from recognizing the urges or experiences that originally caused them.

If in the dead of night we hear a robber in the house, we no longer, like a child, pull the covers up over our head and pretend there's no one there. Instead we gird ourselves to confront him. This confronting, while it lasts, may be unpleasant, though in the long run far less unpleasant than letting ourselves be secretly robbed of such precious possessions as the ability to work successfully, marry happily,

---

* There is no secret about the other kind; they can be found in psychiatric textbooks and books on abnormal psychology. But since they are more useful to doctors than to laymen, they are left out here. For students and anyone wishing to venture into the fine print, a bibliography is included.

and have fun in life. Or the confronting may not turn out to be half so bad as we anticipated because the robber, instead of being a dangerous giant, is nothing but a panicky small child.

Experiences become repressed when they are unconsciously felt to be too great a threat to the person. But what is unconsciously felt to be a threat to a three-year-old may seem only poignant to a thirteen-year-old and perhaps almost funny to a thirty-year-old. Yet the thirty-year-old is as thoroughly prevented from gaining conscious access to his own repressed material as he was when three: the repressing power or unconscious policeman still stands in his way.

This unconscious policeman, like the rest of the deeply unconscious, is impervious to time and to reason. Like Horatio at the bridge, it is not to be budged by anybody's arguments. It is there to protect the conscious self from pain, and this it does with such vigor and momentum that sometimes it ends up causing a pain worse than the one it was originally trying to ward off.

For example, quite a few soldiers in the last war were brought to hospitals totally blind, although nothing could be found wrong with their eyes as such. As it turned out later, they had been faced with a sight so shattering that their unconscious policeman, in order to protect the conscious self, had immediately blacked out their vision, and also, in this particular respect, their memory as well. Out of sight was out of mind.

They remembered nothing of the experience and they could see nothing after the experience. The non-remembering was a relief from pain, but the lasting inability to see was too high a price to pay for such relief. They wanted their vision back, and in order to get it, they had to remember and re-live, with the help of the doctor, the terror, the hatred, the disgust, the guilt, whatever were the shattering emotions that the experience had been capable of arousing in them. For a while they suffered deeply—in some cases the blindness was a symbolic expression of a deep yearning to have been innocent, helpless, and outside the range of blame, and together with the return of memory and vision the terrible possibility of personal guilt also returned—but eventually many of them were able to see again.

Their unconscious policeman had meant well, but like an officious young cop it had rather overdone matters. Here is where the unconscious policeman differs sharply from its conscious counterpart, what we call our conscience. This conscience, in comparison, is like a wise old judge, able to admit all significant evidence, throw out what is unessential or outdated, and then render a reasonable verdict in accordance with the facts.

There is all the difference in the world between the conscious *rejection* of some urge and the unconscious *repression* of it. The resulting outer behavior may be identical but the inner effects are not. When we consciously reject, we know what we are doing. The higher mental processes are brought to bear in forming an intelligent choice that can, if the outer situation changes, also be changed. But when we unconsciously repress, we don't know what we're doing. All we know is that we feel we must act in a particular way lest we suffer a continuing, intense, inner discomfort. This excruciating feeling psychiatrists call unconscious anxiety. It is the billy of the unconscious policeman. It may manifest itself as anxiety we recognize as such, or as depression, or as hatred of ourselves (and the rest of the world), or as meaningless activity, or as irrational behavior, or as indecision, or as physical symptoms ranging all the way from repeated sneezing and chronic exhaustion to paralysis of a limb.

Yet the purpose of this unconscious anxiety, like that of conscious fear, is an essential one: to warn us of the approach of danger. It is extremely useful when the danger is real. But when the danger is no longer real and it continues none the less to be mobilized, it may end up being extremely harmful, since people can hardly be healthy and happy in a state of constant inward terror.

But how, if the policeman and the billy are both completely unconscious, did anyone ever discover how they work? And how on earth can their existence be scientifically verified?

If a series of complicated clinical discoveries can be put into almost absurd briefness, this is what happened:

Sigmund Freud, as a young neurologist working in Vienna with hysterical patients, observed that under hypnosis his patients were able to recall in detail painful experiences of which they had absolutely no memory when conscious. This led him to wonder: must there not be some place *within the person* where these experiences had been not simply forgotten, but where it had been forgotten that they had been forgotten?

Continuing with hypnosis, Freud verified what he had been taught by the great French neurologists, Charcot and Bernheim: that a detailed order given to a patient when he was not conscious was later, consciously, carried out. The patient had no memory of being given the order; all he felt was a strong compulsion to perform that particular act. This led Freud to wonder: must there not be *traffic* between the burial place of our memories and the conscious self?

Discarding hypnosis, Freud and his followers developed (as part of psychoanalytic treatment) free association, which involves the patient's speaking openly to the doctor over long periods of time about whatever comes into his head. The patient, freed from having to justify himself or to be logical or rational, often found himself expressing thoughts and feelings he never knew existed within him. Gradually it came to Freud's notice that what dreams the patient had by night and what memory blocks, slips of the tongue, and mistakes in reading or spelling he had by day were *not haphazard*. Symbolically, they presented clues which, when traced back by the patient with the support of the doctor, led to precisely the same kind of painful unconscious memories that the patients under hypnosis had dredged up. This led Freud to wonder: must there not be

[25

a *director of the traffic* whose aim was to guard the conscious self from being visited by the experiences that he had once unconsciously felt too threatening to him?

Lastly came the most fantastic discovery of all. Freud was not an Adonis, but he found most of his patients falling in love with him. He was not a terrifying man but he found most of his patients fearing and hating him, and, what is more, feeling these conflicting emotions at the same time. What could he have been doing to merit all this emotional attention? He had neither tried to seduce nor to attack his patients, yet they talked and dreamed and acted as if he had.

He finally compared notes with his psychoanalytic pupils and found the same bewildering thing was going on between their patients and them. This led Freud to wonder: Must the patient not be now *re-experiencing* what he had once unconsciously felt toward the key people in his childhood (the mother and father or their substitutes)? Further, did not the doctor through his impersonal, permissive listening somehow release from the custody of the patient's unconscious policeman old, strong urges that, for want of a better object, came to roost on the doctor?

It was as if the personal relationships that had once stung the patient unbearably needed a different personal relationship to withdraw the sting. A patient might intellectually know that he had once both loved and hated his parents or his brothers and sisters, but this knowledge, being conscious, could not penetrate to the deeply unconscious parts of him, which tend to be impervious to time and to reason. He had to feel again, live again, wince again under the stings of this old love and hatred, as directed toward another person, in order finally to reorient these feelings. This unconscious refocusing of feelings by the patient onto the doctor was called "transference" by Freud. Psychiatrists today do not fully understand how it operates but, like the non-engineer who owns a radio, they do know how to make use of it when it is working all right.

Out of these various hypotheses of Freud's, subsequently confirmed by psychiatrists all over the world, there developed the concept that only a small part of man's personality lies above the surface of consciousness and by far the greater

part lies hidden. Like a distant swimmer who might appear, to a baby on the shore, as merely a floating head, there is more to us than meets the eye. Indeed, the swimmer's head wouldn't be there at all were it not for his powerful muscles moving continuously and invisibly below the surface.

The swimmer we call well-balanced is the one who adapts his strokes to the wind and waves and the swimmers near by. But the swimmer who is too much under the control of his unconscious policeman may, no matter what the wind or weather, feel compelled to keep doing the dog paddle, since that was what he learned in childhood. Both swimmers may get to the same end of the lake at the same time, but the one who is more adaptable will have had a happier time and have been a more pleasant companion. He will also, should the big waves of life start splashing around, be more likely to keep his head above water.

Psychiatrists in daily practice have found that the more a patient becomes aware of what goes on beneath the surface of consciousness, the better equipped he is to control his subterranean urges and feelings rather than have them continue to control him. He does not have to like them, but he does have to learn to live with them, in order to achieve that ineffable combination of inner peace and outer usefulness which is called mental health.

As psychiatry has shown, we human beings do not create our own basic urges: they are part of the innate equipment with which we all come into the world. Like electricity, they are forces of nature for whose *existence* we do not need to feel responsible. We still need to feel responsible for what we *do* with these basic urges, but we no longer need to suffer guilt, as did the Victorians, for the questionable thoughts and images and dreams that pop unbidden into our minds. Long ago this lack of control over what occurs within us was dramatized in the legend of the hated emperor who finally agreed to step down if a man could be found capable of sitting all day in a dungeon and *not* thinking of a white elephant. The result, of course, was that the canny old boy stayed safely on his throne.

All of us probably have had murderous fantasies, but few of us have committed murder, or ever will. We realize murder is wrong and we are able to prevent ourselves from acting it out. The people who do commit murder may also realize it is wrong but sometimes they cannot prevent themselves from acting it out. Many of them are what we call mentally ill. By this, psychiatrists do not mean to imply that mental health is the same as virtue or that mental illness is the same as vice. Actually some mental patients are virtuous and self-sacrificing to an inordinate degree, and some normal people are wicked enough to drive others out of their wits. What psychiatrists do mean is that mentally healthy people—sometimes defined as "mild neurotics," people who are not in a state of terrible inner tension because of their repressed urges and experiences—have greater freedom of choice. They are relatively free to refrain from doing what appears to their conscious selves as wrong or silly or harmful, whereas mentally ill people sometimes feel impelled not only to do what they know to be wrong or silly or harmful but even to keep repeating it.

One escape that is open to us all from this inner tension is laughter. Freud's theory was that through humor we can pleasantly bring to the surface feelings that might otherwise remain repressed and straining at the anchor chain. As he put it:

> By its repudiation of the possibility of suffering, humor takes its place in the great series of methods devised by the mind of man for evading . . . suffer[ing] . . . a series which begins with neurosis and delusions and includes intoxication, self-induced states of abstraction, and ecstasy.

In other words, humor is one benign way of mastering our forbidden urges, of rising above our forbidden fears, of bearing the unbearable for a moment. We may never con-

sciously admit that within ourselves lies an urge to do away
with a member of our own family, but we can guffaw over
a cartoon in which wife and husband or parent and child
kill each other so diabolically and with such gleeful abandon
that its very absurdity insulates us momentarily from any
feeling of reality and therefore of responsibility.

As Freud pointed out, the relief of laughter, besides being
only temporary, must also sneak up on us. If it can be seen
coming by our unconscious policeman, the billy will drive

it away, and conscious straining for it won't help. We can
no more deliberately get the point of a joke than we can
not think of a white elephant: the point either hits us on
the head or it passes by. In this respect laughter is like sleep:
it must catch us unawares. The joke-teller's "stop me if
you've heard this" indicates our recognition that humor

rapidly reaches a stage of diminishing returns, and that when we can anticipate the clincher, either through familiarity or through a clumsy build-up, our unconscious policeman is alerted and we can, at best, only smile a sickly smile.

If a joke, on the other hand, is new and well-presented and funny to other people and we still can't laugh, it may be striking too close to home. As Don Quixote said: "Tis ill . . . [joking] . . . of halters in the house of a man that was hanged." If a joke touches on an area that our unconscious policeman has under close surveillance, we will either not get the point, or will get it all right but not think it is at all funny.

If anyone doesn't believe this, let him try telling a bathroom story to a prim lady of over seventy and watch her unconscious policeman go to work in the set of her lips and the crease of her frown. Or, on second thought, if he loves her and doesn't want to arouse in her the unconscious anxiety of the policeman's billy, he'd better not try. For she was brought up when Queen Victoria was still alive, when no "nice" person apparently ever had to go to the bathroom, and when a baby's natural curiosity about the eliminative function was met by adult shock and severe reprimand. Still, if there happens to be some genial older person in the room who will laugh with the story-teller, the old lady may give forth an embarrassed titter. Somehow when we feel that another person's unconscious policeman is letting down the bars, our own is more likely to relax, particularly if the other person is older than we are, or about our own age. The laughter of children, being not so reassuring to an adult, is probably therefore not so contagious as that of other adults.

Thus it appears to be no accident that man, the only animal with an unconscious policeman (as far as we know) should also be the only animal to laugh (as far as we know). Man has long been distinguished as "the laughing animal," hyenas notwithstanding. The power and endurance of the human ability to laugh was brought home to the authors during the preparation of this book. After hours and hours of looking over cartoons and arguing the various philosophic and psychological theories of mirth (all of which, except Freud's, were subsequently left out), one person could still tip his chair back with "Oh, say, that reminds me of the one about . . ." and off the others would go again as if they'd never heard a joke before. (The urge to laugh, in civilized man, seems to be almost as irrepressible as the urges of hunger and sex. Fortunately students of humor can still get laughs just as butchers can still enjoy eating steak and obstetricians can still enjoy making love.)

It is therefore without any fear of spoiling the reader's enjoyment of the cartoons that this short analysis of laughter has been included. When the reader finds himself tickled by some cartoon, this may be because he is laughing off a certain amount of inner tension, or it may be because he is tempted to laugh off as worthless the findings of psychiatry. For, if psychiatrists can be laughed out of court, then so can their evidence that man is not so fully the conscious master of himself as he would like to be.

Over the last twenty years, in popular magazines, there has been a steadily increasing number of cartoons and jokes portraying the psychiatrist as exaggeratedly hateful, stupid, venal, sexy, or crazy. As human beings (and most psychi-

atrists are human beings), psychiatrists find themselves
somewhat chagrined by this hostile picture of themselves in
the public mind, but as objective scientists (and most of
them fit into that category too), they are fascinated. It
looks to them as if the civilized natives of twentieth-century
America were trying symbolically to kill or worship them,
at least in effigy, because of the small glowing flashlight
they carry in their hands. Evidence of the symbolic killing
is the extreme hostility of the cartoons; evidence of the
symbolic worship is their extreme number. Since it is no
fun to debunk someone unless he has already been placed
on some kind of pedestal, it is interesting to note that during the period when the number of cartoons poking fun at
psychiatrists has been increasing, the number poking fun at
ministers has been decreasing.

In any event, the main thing is for the flashlight currently
being held by the psychiatrists to be allowed to spread its
flickering beams as far and wide as possible. Psychiatrists
don't have all the answers, or even many of the answers, but
they do know more about what goes on under the surface of
consciousness than other human beings, except for rare
creative or prophetic geniuses.

As the valiant reader grasps the flashlight and goes from
here on his safari into the uncharted wilderness of himself,
he has the psychiatrist's assurance that no matter how exotic
or depressing the blooms he comes upon may seem, these
have their counterpart, to some extent at least, in his baby
brother, his mother-in-law, his boss, and the authors.

For it is out of the same basic urges and feelings that
each one of us builds his own unique and irreplaceable self.

[33

And how *that* comes about only future research may tell, although even with all the research in the world a final answer will never be discovered by psychiatrists or by any other human being. As Gustave Flaubert has written:

> *The day on which the answer is found will be this planet's last. Life is an eternal problem; so is history and everything else. Fresh figures are always being added to the sum. How can you count the spokes of a turning wheel?*

Basic Urges and Feelings

◇◇

There is no absurdity so palpable but that it may be firmly planted in the human head if you only begin to inculcate it before the age of five, by constantly repeating it with an air of great solemnity.

SCHOPENHAUER

ONE THING THAT CAN'T BE SAID about the basic urges * of man, any more than it can be said to the face of a friend not seen for years, is: "My, how you've changed." For they haven't—not in the thousands of years of which we have any record. A modern audience will still respond to a tragedy of Sophocles with the same "proper purgation of the emotions" that Aristotle observed in his contemporaries. And there are no feelings that psychiatry has unearthed in twentieth-century men and women that weren't chronicled in the Bible.

Of course, civilized man does not always act out his urges. Because his world is so highly inhabited, his behavior must

---

* What are here referred to as urges are also known, by the professionals concerned, as drives, needs, and instincts. By urge is meant strong action that is basic to survival; by feeling, the emotions aroused in us as a result of the satisfaction or frustration of the urges.

[35

be highly inhibited. Some of his urges, however, can be denied more easily than others. The urge to breathe, for example, can hardly be denied at all. We can exert all our will power not to breathe, but eventually our instinct for survival will win out. Even the yogis, who have developed elaborate rules for breathing, cannot stop it entirely. Nor, since there's plenty of oxygen available and one person's breathing doesn't bother another (except at night during snores), is there any particular reason for us to try.

The urge to eat is more controllable than the urge to breathe, although if we want to survive we can no more go entirely without food than without air. And the urge of sex is one of the most controllable of all. (Plenty of people appear to pay little attention to it, while plenty of others appear to pay little attention to anything else.) Despite the urge of sex being so compressible that any one individual can go through life without ever directly acting it out, it is also so compelling that, whether encouraged to do so by their society or not, enough individuals to keep the human race going have been acting it out. Other urges that, like sex, can be denied direct expression by the individual but are essential to the survival of the race are the urge to be safe and protected (dependence) and the urge to master the world (aggression).

Although these basic urges of man do not vary from era to era, the way they are expressed does vary greatly from culture to culture and within the same culture from time to time and from class to class.

For example, our own Greco-Judeo-Christian culture considers it wrong to kill another human being, and yet the

Thugos tribe in India (from which our word "thug" is derived) insists that a youth must kill a man (from another tribe) before being admitted to adult privileges. In our culture, moreover, during wartime it is considered so right to kill a man (from another tribe) that we award the nation's

"*On a good windy day their veils blow up and you can see their mouths and chins.*"

KETCHAM © Saturday Evening Post

highest honor for excellence in killing. Not so long ago, in our own culture too, an insulted gentleman was permitted —even encouraged—to kill another gentleman by dueling, although if the insult came from a lower-class man, a horse-whipping was considered more appropriate. (Americans do not like to think that there are "classes" in our culture, but sociologists and anthropologists agree that these subcultures do exist, though less firmly fixed than in Europe, Asia, or Africa.)

Along with these various urges which we share to some extent with the higher animals, there is one impulse that seems to be unique to man. It appears in all cultures of which we have any knowledge, usually in connection with some system of religious belief. This is the impulse to do what we consider right and to avoid doing what we consider wrong.

Whether the intense importance of moral values to human beings (through both the unconscious policeman and the conscious conscience) comes as a result of evolutionary mutation or by divine hand, or by both, will long be argued. But what cannot be argued is that human beings, in order to live at peace with themselves as well as with their fellows, feel impelled to follow a scheme of right and wrong which, by and large, is the same as the one they were brought up to believe in. And when they do not follow it they fall prey to that extraordinarily unpleasant sensation known as guilt. (Careful experimentation with animals has shown that they suffer from fear of punishment rather than from guilt for performing forbidden acts, beginning to cringe only when confronted by the person whom they fear, and apparently never losing sleep over their own past misdemeanors, whether these have been discovered or not.)

If someone tries to tell a man that his scheme of values is faulty or that he or his immediate family is not unconsciously as well as consciously sticking by these values, he tends to close his mind against the anxiety such questioning stirs up. Yet, curiously, he does not mind if *other* people live according to other values or if other people, believing in his values, do not carry them out.

It doesn't particularly bother us to learn that in the days of the Egyptian Pharaohs no one was believed good enough to marry the royal prince except one of his sisters—but it does bother us to be told that even in the furthest recesses of our own or our brother's or sister's unconscious mind lies

*"I'm not sure, but I think he's from the Yale
Psychological School."*

ROSE © *The New Yorker Magazine, Inc.*

the germ of an incestuous love. It doesn't particularly bother us to learn that some Eskimos still send their aged parents out into the snow to die—but it does bother us to be told that deep within ourselves and our children lies the unconscious germ of a wish toward matricide or patricide. It doesn't particularly bother us to learn of our friends' infidelities (indeed, sometimes it's rather fun)—but it does bother us to be told that unconsciously we and our spouse and our parents are not completely monogamous. And it not only doesn't bother us, but we actually pay money for the privilege of sitting in a darkened theater and watching the playing out of human urges toward murder, madness, suicide, and a limited amount of homosexuality (in Hamlet

[39

and Othello), or torturing, lust, and avarice (in Lear and Macbeth).

There must be something within us that vibrates in response to these forbidden acts by other people (newspaper

ADDAMS © *The New Yorker Magazine, Inc.*

circulation-managers have long known the pulling power of a fully described rape). Psychiatry believes this something is the repressed opposite core of our acceptable feelings. (As was noted in Chapter I, repressed feelings do not die—or even fade away—but continue like submerged buoys to try to spring back to the surface.)

Dr. Eugen Bleuler first formulated the theory that all

strong feelings have an opposite core that is usually repressed, and, as imperfect man had long suspected, no human emotion ever exists in a pure state: deep within love
lies a repressed core of hate, deep within sexual desire lies

ARNO © *The New Yorker Magazine, Inc.*

a repressed core of fear, and deep within strivings to master
the world lies a repressed core of wanting to be taken care
of. Like the pushmipullyu of Dr. Dolittle (another great

[*41*

psychiatrist), our feelings have two opposite heads and often try to go in both directions at once.

This concept goes by the name of ambivalence, and is perhaps not unrelated to other opposites in our world such as light and dark and heat and cold. Many years ago the oppositeness of our feelings was dramatized in Stevenson's Dr. Jekyll and Mr. Hyde, and even earlier in Congreve's oft-quoted

> Heaven has no rage like love to hatred turned
> Nor hell a fury like a woman scorned.

As a matter of fact, none of the fundamental psychiatric discoveries is new. Nor is this surprising, since the basic feelings of man have not changed, and since the great artistic and prophetic geniuses have always intuitively known what was going on inside us. Although the Victorians were horrified when Freud announced that the feelings they considered "unnatural" were not unnatural at all but were part of our innate equipment, many of them were familiar with the same idea as expressed by a minister born in 1555, John Bradford, who said, while watching evildoers being taken to the place of execution: "But for the grace of God, there goes John Bradford."

Even the basic theory of psychiatry's newest offspring, psychosomatic medicine, was formulated by Nietzsche almost a hundred years ago:

Contentment preserves one even from catching cold. Has a woman who knew that she was well dressed ever caught cold? No, not even when she had scarcely a rag to her back.

42]

Yet this same great philosopher also wrote things so open to misinterpretation that Hitler was able to quote Nietzsche as justification for his own most heinous acts. Thus, although the chief discoveries of psychiatry had previously been stated by some genius, these earlier statements were often mixed in with others that were of no value or were actually false. Since a genius is not necessarily freer from bias than anyone else, and since he rarely checks his conclusions against anything but his own hunches, everything a genius works on doesn't always turn out to be a work of genius. When we lesser creatures quarrel with some of his conclusions, it may even be we who are right. The unique value of sound psychiatric writing, on the other hand, is that although the writer may be no genius his conclusions are based only on what has been observed over and over in patients of every size, shape, sex, and background, and subsequently verified as objectively as possible. Therefore we cannot lightly dismiss these observations, even though we sometimes wish we could.

As human beings, psychiatrists can respond to Keats's

> Beauty is truth, truth beauty, that is all
> Ye know on earth, and all ye need to know,

for in a sense their lives are devoted to the search for truth. But as scientists they are bound to report that for hours a day they are confronted with the sufferings of patients whose true feelings may turn out to be not a bit beautiful, and whose beautiful feelings may turn out to be not a bit true. Indeed, it is often the patient's extreme unconscious reluctance to face up to the truth of his own unbeautiful feelings that leads to his later suffering. He is, however, perfectly willing to admit the existence of such unbeautiful feelings in other people, particularly in the psychiatrist.

While there is no floor to what we are willing to believe about other people and no ceiling to what we are willing to believe about ourselves, at the same time we are also filled with self-doubt and anxiety. However unintentionally, we seem to operate by double standards, one for ourselves, another for other people; one for ourselves consciously and another unconsciously. Perhaps this is a sensible way to resolve the conflicts that inevitably beset us, the conflicts between our basic urges and the rules of our society, the conflicts between one basic urge and another, and the conflicts between the basic urges and the repressed core of their own opposites.

Or might there not be a more sensible way to align our inward vision so that we no longer see several images, but see only one? Might we not try to integrate our standards for ourselves and other people and also our conscious and unconscious standards for ourselves? For just as both other people and ourselves are valuable and unique, so the higher centers of consciousness and also the deeper centers of the unconscious are valuable and unique. Our task is not to set one above the other, but to synchronize them so that we get the best out of both and get both to work together.

But how to single out our conscious and unconscious standards so that what we think and what we feel can be brought into closer alignment? Man is an indissoluble

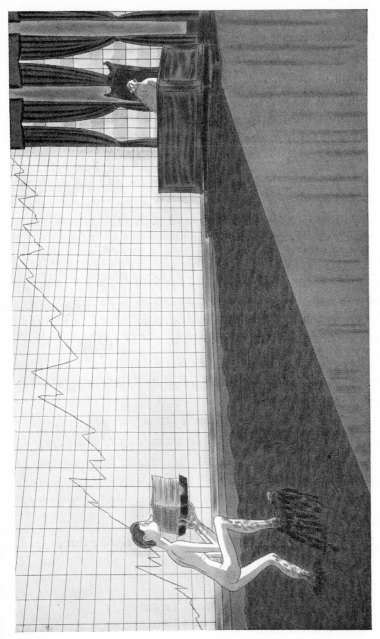

What am I doing here?

© Abner Dean

whole. No longer do we, as in ages past, consider "mind" and "heart" as separate. We now know, on the basis of clinical evidence, that the thoughts of the mind and the feelings of the heart exist together in the nervous system of the body, moving by some kind of neurological impulse back and forth in the brain from consciousness to unconsciousness, and under certain conditions being prevented from reaching consciousness by what we call the unconscious policeman.

Which are the thoughts and feelings that the unconscious policeman has been found to block? Many of them, as psychiatrists have discovered through their study of healthy as well as sick people, have to do with those very urges which, although essential to the survival of the race, must be firmly controlled by each individual in order for us all to live together. Yet, as was noted in the first chapter, conscious control (or rejection) is very different from unconscious blocking (or repression). It is as if something about the way we who are adult today were taught to handle these urges had caused us to repress a far higher proportion of them than necessary. Certainly many of us, when these basic urges are stirred up, give evidence of suffering considerable unconscious tension.

What are these urges? They have been described in many different ways. Here they are presented, with some diffidence, boiled down to an essential and inclusive three:

1. The urge to be safe and protected (security and dependence).
2. The urge to master the world (aggression).
3. The urge to unite with others (love and sex).

In taking these up separately, an attempt is made to show how each is shared to some extent with the animals; how each develops according to predictable biological patterns; and how each poses problems that, although they cannot ever be completely solved, might well be lessened if we became more aware of their existence.

Security and Dependence *

All animals, as far as we know, develop protection against the elements and against other animals. They grow fur, shed fur, are colored in such a way as to blend in with the landscape, find caves to hibernate in, all without apparently giving it any thought. A bird flying south does not read brochures on the beauties of Florida and Georgia; he simply takes to the air in order not to freeze to death. Perhaps because the urge to be safe and warm is so instinctive in animals, the mothers seem to understand immediately what their babies crave in this connection. And, as a matter of fact, the period during which the babies need a mother to satisfy their wants is relatively short. Calves and colts are on their feet right after birth, chicks peck for food almost before they are completely out of the shell, and some fish swim off immediately after being hatched, never having laid eyes on either parent.

In contrast, the human infant arrives in a totally helpless condition and takes about a year to learn to maneuver on

---

* This term to the psychiatrist means an attitude of relying on other people for the satisfaction of our needs for food, warmth, safety, and comfort, and assuming responsibility neither for ourselves nor for them. Financial dependence (the layman's meaning) fits into this picture, but is only a small part of it.

[47

his wobbly bowlegs. He takes even longer to communicate his needs to his parents in a comprehensible way. This prolonged period of human helplessness is believed to be connected with our being the most highly developed creature on the evolutionary scale. It is as if man's complicated brain and higher centers of consciousness made it imperative that he take his own sweet time about growing up to them.

In any event, the human infant emerges at the moment of birth from what appears to have been a completely satisfying environment into that cold cruel world where for the first time he has to breathe and eliminate and eat for himself. Animals of course have to do these things too, but eating is far easier for them because, from the very beginning, they can squirm their way to their mother when she doesn't come to them, and quite soon they can use their teeth and muscles to forage for themselves. But the human infant, like the mountain, must wait for Mohammed to come to it. So uniquely helpless is the human being for the first weeks of life that he continues to lie in whatever position he was put down in, and unless a nipple is placed in the immediate vicinity of his mouth he has no way of satisfying his hunger. What may seem both wonderful and terrifying to him is that when food and warmth and cuddling do come, it is as if they came in direct response to his wishes; as if, simply by needing something, he could magically cause it to appear—sometimes.

Of course no one knows for sure what an infant feels and thinks, but it is now believed that for the first weeks of life the infant remains unable to differentiate inner and outer reality: hunger (inner) is not distinguished from the bottle (outer). For a time he seems to himself to *be* the world, and only gradually, as his senses and his mind develop, is the painful fact forced on him that instead of being the world, he is only a tiny and helpless part of it.*

Many experts believe this very first adjustment is the most difficult and agonizing of all: that nothing in later life, except possibly some combat experiences, compares with the baby's desperation when he first feels hunger or cold or loneliness and isn't immediately comforted. Nor can this suffering of the baby be prevented even by the most careful parents, since the baby has not yet enough sense of time and space to understand that bottle-in-the-warmer will soon mean bottle-in-the-mouth, nor enough reasoning power to figure out that since he has always been provided with warmth in the past, chances are he will be provided with warmth again. Instead, each time, he feels totally lost and alone in a world he never made. Nor are his violent paroxysms of screaming inappropriate to what he is probably feeling at the time.

When someone, usually the mother, does come, the baby's relief and joy know no bounds. In adult life the only thing comparable might be the sensation of an inmate of the death house who has just received word of the governor's pardon. And the baby's bliss in at last being fed and held and cherished and protected perhaps stays with us all,

---

* Certain schizophrenics are believed never to have made this primary adjustment and continue to confuse what *is* true (that they are helpless in their environment) with what they *wish* to be true (that they be all-powerful). To a slight extent all of us may suffer from such confusion at times.

at least in deepest memory, throughout our lives. Here, temporarily, is paradise, where we have everything we want and nothing is demanded of us in return.

But only too soon things do begin to be demanded of us in return. In order to be held and cherished by our parents, we have to be "good," and when we persist in clinging to them we are told "not to be a big baby." American society, perhaps because of our pioneering background, demands emotional independence of its children at a fairly early age, particularly in the case of boys.

"Oh, John, this is the day I dreaded. Baby just took his first step."

ATKINS © *Collier's*

By this time, however, the mothers, whom nature seems to endow with an almost unlimited need-to-be-needed, and the fathers, who also exhibit a tendency to mope when the chicks fly the coop, have developed an emotional dependence on the child—not, be it said, to be protected, but to be protector. Thus emotional weaning is hard on both parent and child, and the child may sense that behind the parents' outspoken desire for him to "grow up, for Pete's sake" lies the unspoken opposite. It's even possible that this feeling on the part of the parents comes from their identifying themselves with their child: in this way they may achieve a vicarious satisfaction of that part of their own yearning for security which was never fully satisfied by their parents and was presumably repressed.

For we in America frown on the enjoyment of helplessness, particularly by men. Occasionally a wife will say tolerantly: "You ought to see my husband when he's sick, he's just a big baby." But she would probably not be so tolerant if, when he was well, he still wanted to lie around and be waited on. Or we will smile understandingly when a college boy (especially is this true of the so-called upper classes) goes on an occasional bat and sucks so well from another kind of bottle that he goes back (regresses) in his behavior to the point where he again babbles nonsense, is unable to walk, and has to be "put to bed." Yet, if he continued this behavior beyond college we would not be so understanding.

Our American picture of the ideal male is a he-man, self-reliant rather than dependent, and extremely ambitious and competitive in his attempts to supply his family with the material things of life. We rarely remember that, for example, in ancient Greece the most highly respected men were sedentary philosophers who would probably have looked upon our steak-eating, chest-pounding, Tarzan-yelling ideal of manliness as brutish and vulgar. To them, as to the Orthodox Jews, attending to the material needs of the family was "woman's work" and far beneath the dignity of

"Alfred, when you are late returning from shore leave, a tardiness excuse from your mother will not suffice."

HUMFREVILLE © *Collier's*

the mighty male, whose business was to concern himself with matters of high spiritual import.

On the other hand, even in our society, men are expected to be gentle in the home, indulgently smiling at the antics of their children and the whims of their wives. And despite the fact that on weekdays they are expected to rise in the world at the expense of their neighbor, on Sundays they are exhorted to love and co-operate with him. Added to these conflicts which society imposes is one which biology imposes; namely, that the male is not totally "masculine" any more than the female is totally "feminine," all of us having many more hormones and sexual enjoyments in common than is generally supposed.

As for women, what our society expects of them is perhaps even more confusing. A girl is encouraged to be dependent, financially and in every other way, first on her parents and then on her husband. When there is money enough in the family, fathers and husbands are likely to take a dim view of the ladyfolks' going out into the world in competition with them. Yet the minute anything happens to the father or the husband, the girl or woman is expected to be equipped to support herself, and perhaps small children as well.

In the atomic age, women can hardly feel secure in their dependent helplessness, and as a matter of fact many of them don't want to. Women in America have fought too long and too hard to break away from their status of second-class citizen to be willing to sit back and be "feminine" beings rather than human beings. They would rather face the conflicts that their strivings for economic, professional, and political independence involve for them and for the men whose affection they desire. One disgruntled gentleman of the old school has stated the problem from his point of view: "These modern girls compete with us downtown all day and then in the subway coming home they still expect us to give up our seats for them." But from the girl's point of view it is perhaps even more baffling to find that one minute a man admires her because she is helpless and impressed by his superior strength, and the next minute he expects her to paddle her end of the canoe with power and skill.

This sudden reversal of the female role demanded by males is particularly apparent when the babies begin to ar-

"On second thought . . . I think I agree with my worthy opponent!"

LINDA WALTER © *King Features Syndicate, Inc.*

rive. Overnight the tender and dependent bride is expected to be a Rock of Gibraltar as far as the young are concerned. She finally gathers the strength to be on call for the children on a twenty-four-hour basis and to enjoy it—and then all of a sudden they are gone and she is criticized for Momism if she regrets their going. (Actually, the so-called in-law problem is usually a direct-parent problem: it is the clinging of the parent to the grown son or daughter that causes the conflict with the young in-law who wants that son or daughter to be his own grown mate.) Finally she learns to adjust to that deafening silence of a childless house—and its concurrent unemployment—and even to enjoy that, and then all of a sudden the grandchildren arrive and she is expected to be on twenty-four-hour call again if needed, though well out of the way when not.

Coupled with these separate problems about dependence for women and for men are the joint ones caused by old age. Often, at the height of their wisdom, working men or women have their jobs cut out from under them by illness, compulsory retirement, or other causes. If they are lucky enough to have their mate still around, they then become reliant on him or her for all-day companionship despite perhaps, over the past forty years, having only seen the creature during a hurried breakfast and late dinner.

In the old days when America was largely an agricultural nation there often was room on the farm for the old folks and plenty of mild chores for them to do and to feel needed through doing. Today, in our largely urban nation with its tiny homes crammed with modern conveniences, there is neither place nor job for elderly parents. Modern science has for a long time been successful in prolonging the years of life, but it has only recently turned its attention to guiding these years toward constructive and happy living.

Last, and even worse than the growing helplessness and

unwantedness of old age, comes the loss of the life-partner through death. In America it is mostly the women who are left behind, and their bereavement is probably as close to unbearable as are the feelings of the infant who believes itself deserted. (Actually, tiny babies whose mothers have died show evidence of depression very close to what in older people is called grief.) So awful is bereavement to human beings that it is the only emotional area in which no amusing cartoons seem to exist. Out of thirty thousand there were some cartoons on matters as horrendous as the atom bomb and as awe-inspiring as God, but there were none on that final loneliness and helplessness with which we all, sooner or later, must come to terms unless, like the good, we die young and let the members of our family do the suffering.

In our society, yearnings for protection without responsibility are never fully satisfied, and are rarely recognized as such until perhaps at the very end of life. When, therefore, we feel desolate, anxious, and sorry for ourselves, when we tend to overeat and overdrink or feel panicky about the future, all for no apparent reason, it may simply be our old repressed urge of dependence trying to force its way to the surface.

Aggression *

If our ancestors at all evolutionary levels had not ag-

---

* To the psychiatrist, this term includes attempts to master our environment and other people, to exert power, to throw our weight around. The "aggressive," energetic, and willful person (the layman's meaning) fits into this picture but is only a small part of it. To the psychiatrist, aggressive is almost the opposite of dependent and often leads to hostile and destructive feelings and acts.

gressively struck out in self-defense and in search of food, the human race would not be here today. Of course, ironically, it may not be here much longer if we put to use the superweapons of aggression which our relatively new (in terms of evolution) faculty of reason has enabled us to develop.

Animals attack with their big muscles, teeth, or claws, though a few, like porcupines and skunks, have specialized skills. The end purpose of animal attack is to kill, either in self-defense or for food. As far as we know, animals do not feel guilt or anxiety about killing; they simply, as with growing or shedding fur, go ahead and do it in order to survive. And, as a matter of fact, our own laws excuse killing if it occurs in self-defense, either individual (as in protecting our person or our home against a robber) or national (as in war).

But man begins early to feel guilt and anxiety about his aggressive urges. Again, to start as near the beginning as possible: when the infant's muscles and teeth develop, he no longer feels so helpless and quite naturally begins to reach out for what he wants and to strike or bite or kick when he is frustrated. This results in his being punished by the very person whom he loves best and on whose love he is still dependent for his existence.

This sets up one of the first big conflicts within the child, who can neither face losing the love of his parent nor yet fully control his almost-reflex kicking and biting when faced with an obstacle. Furthermore, when he is punished by his parent, he naturally feels resentment bordering on hatred. Yet how can he be hating the very person he loves? So unbearable is this kind of conflict to the unformed personality of the small child that he is likely to repress it entirely. Not only will he no longer openly attack his parent by tooth or claw, which for the sake of family harmony is all to the

"You mean all these years I just thought I had a happy childhood?"

GIBSON © *The New Yorker Magazine, Inc.*

good, but he will also no longer even recognize that he ever wanted to, which for the sake of his own inner harmony may not be all to the good.

Our homes, our schools, our churches combine to hammer into the child's head that he should at all times and places, consciously and unconsciously, honor his father and his mother. Of course fathers and mothers do a great deal for us and of course we owe them a great deal. But need this mean that after we are adult they should retain so direct a road to our innards that their praise and blame still affect our ability to eat and sleep and work and live? Or that when they die we should feel a pervasive guilt, a desperate "Oh, if only I had been a better son or daughter"? Honoring parents is fine (the authors of this book, all of whom have children, feel this very strongly), but it need not turn into an unconscious burning of incense at the shrine. Even Jesus assured his followers in no uncertain terms that there are things more important in the world than filial affection: "He that loveth father or mother more than me is not worthy of me."

Yet many adults today react with shock to the idea that they may not have loved their own parents a hundred per cent, or that their own children do not always love them. They may recognize consciously that most of the progress in the world has come from children's kicking over the parental traces but they themselves are unwilling to say—or even to think—that in moments of anger they ever wished their parents out of the way.

The unconscious anxiety that prevents adults from recognizing their old hostile feelings toward their parents sometimes also affects their attitude toward authoritative (parental) people like their boss or national leader. In Germany and Russia, in relation to the dictator, grown men and women have, like uncritical small children, been hurrying out to do what they were told "because father says so," feeling both relieved and pleased when their efforts—no matter

[59

THE SAD SACK "ORDERS"

SGT. G. BAKER

BAKER © George Baker

how much these may have gone against the grain of human decency—met with his approval.

Here in America some attitudes toward the national leader are perhaps adolescent rather than childish, being characterized less by unthinking docility than by unthinking wild extremes. Our Presidents, particularly Lincoln and Franklin Roosevelt, have been both worshipped to the point of idolatry and also made victims of whispered accusations suitable only to rebellious thirteen-year-olds smoking behind the barn.

Since a small child in our society soon learns not to express aggression openly against his parents—and in many cases no longer even recognizes its existence in relation to them—he may instead try attacking by means of those activities which at birth he had to do for himself and over which he alone has the control; namely, breathing, eliminating, and eating.

Infantile tantrums almost always involve a holding of breath and choking and coughing, and plenty of parental tempers have been exacerbated around the two key-areas of the high-chair and the potty-chair. Here the child, probably unconsciously, feels that the giant parent who can lift him up, put him down, and in other ways frustrate him at will, can now in turn be frustrated.

Because with modern civilization we take for granted our three squares and our comfort stations, we tend to forget the huge importance of eating and eliminating. But let either desire be frustrated for a while and we find it dominates our thoughts. How powerful these urges are is indicated both in the fantasies of mentally ill people and the dreams of normal people, which are frequently permeated by imagery of devouring or eliminating loved or hated objects or persons.

By and large, the less primitive the civilization, the more limited the opportunity for openly expressing adult aggres-

"Watch this! I just switched the signs."

LUNDBERG © *Saturday Evening Post*

sion. In our time there are still unmasked strivings for dominance and power on the part of nations as well as individuals, but attempts are continually being made to limit these. In our own nation there are a few outlets for aggression permitted to both men and women, such as enjoyment of custard-pie-in-the-face movies and football games, and acting as sidewalk superintendents. There are also quite a number permitted to men only, such as administering a deserved punch in the nose or, when in uniform, deadly combat by hand or gun. And lawyers, who are mostly men, are encouraged to cut the ground from under their opponents in court, and businessmen to annihilate their competitors. But because of our prevailing ideal of femininity, women are unlikely to find many permitted outlets for aggression, either in terms of striving for power or of doing harm to other people.

Once an American girl is through school and married, she is not supposed to be in open competition with anyone or to quarrel with the people she sees most of—her children, husband, parents, friends, and grocer. Nor when she goes out in the evening is she expected forcefully to assert her opinions and argue with the men. Is it any wonder that our matrons are famous for their catting or that a family's excelling its neighbors through visible objects like a television set or an automobile is often instigated by "the little woman"? Wives' driving of husbands to expenditures beyond the men's inclinations may be one reason for the popularity of the all-male club. American men may feel more relaxed in the evening with men who have spent much of their aggression during the day than with women who have not.

It may even be conjectured that in America today men are more affected by bottled-up dependence, and women by bottled-up aggression. There may be no cause-and-effect connection, but it is interesting to note that ulcers, a disease considered to be accelerated by unsatisfied yearnings to be loved and protected, have been occurring about five times as frequently in men as in women; and that gall-bladder trouble, involving the production of bile, which since Greek days has been a synonym for anger and venom, has been occurring with noticeably greater frequency in women than in men. Whether milk as a common ulcer-cure helps more in its capacity as an anti-acid or as a symbol of maternal affection is one of the many as yet unexplored facets of the whole problem.

When a person is openly aggressive toward us, at least we know who the enemy is and can guard against him. But when someone's aggressive urge is repressed, we may feel only a diffuse uneasiness when he's around. He may be out-

"A penny for your thoughts, dear."

MARTIN © United Newspapers Magazine Corp.

wardly friendly and himself convinced that it is only because he is concerned over our well-being that he denies us what we ask or criticizes what we do. Indeed, he may be deeply offended if we are unhappy or snippy in his presence, although such manifestations of unconscious self-defense on our part may be as appropriate as guarding our-selves against open aggression would be.

Open aggression, besides often being easier than the un-derground variety to cope with in other people, is also often easier to cope with in ourselves. When we recognize that we are in an ugly mood, we can try to work off what is causing it by attacking unfeeling objects, such as a drawer that needs cleaning out or a log that needs splitting. But when what we feel is a diffuse anxiety or depression, or as if we were being threatened by we know not what, we may not recognize that old angers or hatreds, long since repressed, are even now tugging at the anchor chain.

Love and Sex *

Lower animals, like the amœba, presumably do not feel sexual desire at all. They do not need to, since the foolish things reproduce by splitting down the middle. Higher ani-mals, with the exception of man, make no effort to control the sexual urges that overwhelm them. Nature does their controlling for them by encouraging sexual desire only at certain times in the year. Human beings, on the other hand, feel sexual desire all year long and are expected by our mod-ern Western society to control it all their lives, expressing it directly only toward their one legal spouse.

---

* Love and sex are both included in Freud's concept of sex. When he spoke of feelings being "sexual" he did not mean exclusively genital (the layman's definition) but included all erotic feelings. After all, the Greek god Eros was god of love and play—and thus any enjoyment of being close to other people could be technically called "erotic." Psy-chiatry's understanding of the word sex in general follows Freud's, al-though some members of the profession define it broadly as life-force. Considerable clarification is needed before this controversial word achieves a definite meaning even to the professionals.

The huge power of the sexual urge in man has caused uproar since long before young Paris was inflamed by Helen of Troy, and will undoubtedly continue to. Still, as Kinsey reported, many young men and women are currently living

"I wonder why they put the announcement of Adelaide's sixth marriage on the sports page!"

CURRIE © *Fawcett Publications, Inc.*

through their years of highest sexual potency without adequate outlet, and we all know some married people who have conformed throughout their lives to the strictest interpretation of monogamy.

The emphasis on monogamy by all the civil and religious codes of the West, as well as by many of the East, is perhaps not unrelated to man's tendency to search for oneness in other areas: philosophers have long tried to explain the world in terms of one basic principle; scientists, having reduced everything to matter and energy, are now trying to find the unifying matrix; and more than three thousand years ago in our culture the concept of many gods was thrown out in favor of one God. Yet at the time Moses received the commandment that a man should have but one God, there was no limit set on the number of wives he could have. Solomon, who subsequently built the great temple to the one God, is reported in the Bible to have had no less than seven hundred wives and three hundred concubines. Even today there are millions of people who believe in a man's having as many women at one time as he can face (and support), and millions who have no objection to a man or woman's having as many spouses consecutively, by way of divorce, as he or she can face (and support).

In any event, our Western monogamy seems here to stay. And the choices that it enforces on us often involve considerable compression of the sexual urge. Nor does this problem of compression begin, as the Victorians surmised, in a person's late teens. They were startled half out of their wits when Freud announced that babies come into the world with infantile urges that later, but still in early childhood, develop into erotic urges. "But it's unthinkable," they said. And ironically they were being thoroughly accurate, since to them such an idea *was unthinkable* in that they didn't dare use their conscious reason to think about it. So severely had most of them been punished as babies for the slightest enjoyment of their own bodies that their unconscious policemen would not allow them to become aware of such feelings in themselves or even in others. Babies must be innocent! And in point of fact, they are. But had the Victorians been able to think it through, they might have reasoned that their standards, which demanded that a young man's sexual desires should spring full-blown on his wedding night, and that a young lady's should never spring at all, were unrealistic. An urge as potent and essential to the survival of mankind as the sexual one could hardly be expected to turn on like a lamp when the magic words of the wedding service were pronounced. Just as the baby's urge to suck, immediate at birth, develops, as the teeth grow, into the urge to bite, so does the baby's urge to be held warm and safe by the mother's soft arms and body later develop into the desire to touch a member of the opposite sex and to be touched by him or her.

Freud did not publish his observations in order to shock his contemporaries. What he described was what had forced itself on his attention during his attempts to help sick people, many of whom turned out to be suffering from unconscious anxiety because of their repressed sexual urges. Once they learned to understand and readjust to these, their symptoms disappeared. Furthermore Freud noted that just as sexual desires flower gradually, so do they wane gradually. The change of life (climacterium), which occurs together with definite symptoms in women in their forties or fifties, and without such definite symptoms in many men in their fifties or sixties, does not abruptly mean the end of desire. To pretend that it does or to think that it should has caused untold guilt and shame in older people.

68]

Indeed, in respect to sexual matters, psychiatrists might well adopt as theme song the Negro spiritual: "Nobody Knows the Trouble I've Seen." For, most forms of mental or emotional distress involve, in addition to their other symptoms, some disturbance in the sexual sphere. This does

KOVARSKY © *The New Yorker Magazine, Inc.*

not mean that everyone who has some disturbance in his sexual activity is necessarily ill; indeed it is standard operating procedure for people during the early months of marriage to find all kinds of sexual problems to work their way through. But it does mean that if a person's sexual behavior is satisfying to himself and to his partner and to society, the chances are that, emotionally speaking, he's pretty well off. As for the forms of sexual behavior which our society most strenuously forbids, the so-called perversions or deviations, these have in many cases been traced back to an unconscious blocking of the normal sexual development during childhood or adolescence. Moreover they are often accompanied by terrible inner conflict and suffering which outsiders never suspect. Here is a field in which there is still far more to be known than is already known. But even so, on the basis of present scientific findings, it is safe to assume that sexual deviants are sick people rather than criminals, in need of a doctor far more than a jailer, and that only in the rarest cases does society need to protect itself by locking them up.

As to the normal development of the sexual urge, the baby comes into the world with a craving for cuddling as great as his craving for food. It was found by Dr. Rene Spitz that babies taken from their mothers and given the best of hospital care were none the less pale and listless, without appetite, and unable to learn. "T.L.C.," a doctor's medical prescription, worked wonders. What it meant was Tender Loving Care—that the nurses should take time out to dandle and hug and croon to the babies. The babies perked right up, ate better, made the effort to learn to walk and talk and, through feeling the loving care of another person, became responsive and loving themselves.

Young parents often interpret their baby's first upward motion of the lips, which is really caused by gas, as a welcoming smile, and his reaching out to them for comforting as a sign of love. But many doctors today believe that loving involves an awareness of the needs of the other person, and that therefore the small baby is incapable of love. He is still so unaware of the outer world, so self-absorbed, so busy

staying alive, that until he grows and experiences the love
of others he cannot be expected to feel love for others.

After all, since the baby starts out thinking that his
mother's breast or the bottle is a part of himself, it must
take time—years—for him to grasp the fact that other people have needs apart from his own. Yet only after he has
learned this can he feel that the needs of other people
should matter to him. There are plenty of people who have
reached adulthood still incapable of this feeling. They don't
mean to be selfish—they simply are, like the baby, self-
imprisoned.

It is usually after the baby has become aware of his
mother's separate existence that he becomes aware of his
father's. Depending on how the father acts, the baby may
learn to rely on him as if he were a substitute mother (the
highest compliment a baby can pay) or as if he were a
dangerous rival for the mother's vitally needed time and
attention.

Gradually, as the child's limbs develop, he comes into
conflict with grim reality. The first encounter is with hard
playpen sides and slippery floors. This conflict is relatively
bearable because mother—or some adult—is usually around
to pick him up and soothe his battered soul and body.
Soon, cheerfully, he is willing to try again, perhaps in a new
and better way; and eventually he learns to handle himself
and the objects around him.

The second form of conflict, with the parental "No, no,"
is a much worse one. At first the baby experiments to see
what this funny noise is all about and, oh horrors, finds
himself being scolded or slapped, a most unpleasant new

[71

sensation. Even worse, when he reaches out for comforting, he finds that the new enemy is none other than the oldest friend. And by her face and voice he can sense that no friendliness will be forthcoming from *that* source for some time. He is left with no one to turn to, feeling as lonely and frightened as he used to feel as an infant when he yearned for food and didn't get it. So he goes back and does just what he did then: he howls.

What the child feels at such times could only be matched in our adult life if the earth on which we stand were suddenly both to fall away from under us and also to reach out and hit us. Yet even the most solicitous parents cannot entirely prevent their child's suffering these feelings. Modern living includes too many mortal hazards, like gas stoves and automobiles, for parents to risk administering only a gentle rebuke to the child who, by way of these, is endangering his life. For the child's own sake they must be sure to teach him a lesson that he won't forget or ignore even once.

Eventually, of course, no matter what he has done, his mother forgives him, wipes away the tears, and tells him next time to be a "good" child. And how he wants to! Defying the "No, no," is no fun at all—he can't bear the feeling of being outside the circle of his mother's arms and love. He hugs her tight, virtually strangling the poor woman, and inwardly vows never to defy her again. What he does not yet know is that this will be impossible.

For the next thing he finds is that his nice squashy diaper, which never appeared to displease his mother before, is suddenly greeted with a "No, no," or "Dirty, dirty," and he is popped upon a hard, cold, circular seat and forced to feel cold breezes where they were never felt before. With parts of his body thus exposed, he does some exploring and discovers that pleasant feelings result from his pushing and pulling in one particular area. Even more surprising, this action on his part arouses a further and louder "No, no" reaction from his mother. From the way she acts, there must be something wrong with this whole part of him.

Another thing that happens to the baby around this time is that his nice old bottle is suddenly replaced with a weird-tasting mush, which he mouths around for a while and then treats in the only possible way; namely, by spitting out— only to be greeted with more "No, no's" from this now so hard-to-please parent. And his irresponsible arms and legs, which once were kissed and laughed at, are suddenly disapproved of when they happen into contact with dishes or tender parts of other people.

Sometimes near this stage he finds that a hateful, wailing something called "a little sister" or "brother" has sneaked in when he wasn't looking and is claiming most of his mother's attention. The child's feeling in this respect could be compared to the way one of his parents might feel if the other came home with a new spouse, making a great fuss over him or her and expecting the newcomer to be welcomed with open arms as a matter of course by the original one. All in all, it's a tough, mean world, and about the only thing a small person can depend on to have fun with is his very own self.

Whether the child's pleasure in his own body, as through thumb-sucking or self-handling, results primarily from physiological or from psychological development, no one knows.

The indications are that while almost every small child either openly or secretly indulges for a while in some such form of infantile self-love, an extreme or unduly prolonged indulgence may coincide with what the child feels to be

"A baby sister's all right—but there's a lot of things we needed worse."

GAREL © *Saturday Evening Post*

withdrawal of parental love. In adolescence, on the other hand, the general and sometimes extreme return to the joys of childhood seems to coincide with the maturing of the reproductive organs and the concurrent increase of sexual tension.

Whatever its primary cause, the small child's interest in his own body usually precedes his interest in other people's bodies. This subsequent curiosity is equally widespread and often leads to a repeated comparison by the child of his own body with those of contemporaries and parents. The

"It's a little play they worked out."

SPARBER © *Collier's*

story of the little girl seeing her mother in the bathtub and asking: "Why am I so plain and you're so fancy?" is just as true of little boys and their fathers.*

When little boys haven't been told "what little girls are made of," they may fear, when they first see or hear about a little girl undressed, that she has lost a part of her body or

---

* Hair, which may or may not be æsthetically pleasing, often holds an unconscious symbolic connotation of strength, as in the story of Samson.

had it cut off, just as a little girl may fear she is missing a part of her body when she first sees little boys. This plaguing terror on the part of small children often calls for repeated reassurance from both parents until it is outgrown. (There is some question as to whether it can ever be totally outgrown. For example, brave soldiers have admitted that although they do not particularly fear being wounded or even killed, they are in abject terror of a part of the body's being shot away.)

Much has been written about the Œdipus complex. What it seems to boil down to is that small boys for a while wish they had their mother all to themselves—and with this wish comes the natural-enough corollary that it would be nice if the father were not in their way. The core of this wish is that the father would die, but such a thought is too terrifying for the child to face and so he represses it. And the unconscious guilt for harboring such a wish sometimes shows itself in the form of a tit-for-tat fear that the father will kill him—or cut off some part of him.

Little boys outgrow this stage when they learn to admire and trust their father and want to be like him; unconsciously they feel that when they grow to be a big man like Daddy, they can have a lovely lady like Mummy to themselves. Little girls have one more stage to pass through. They start out loving their mother best and wanting their father out of the way, but then they grow to love their father best and want their mother out of the way. Here again, when they learn to admire and trust their mother and want to be like her, they outgrow their unconscious guilt at wanting to kill her: unconsciously they feel that when they grow to be a big lady like Mummy, then they can have a wonder-ful man like Daddy to themselves.

Sometimes these stages in small children are noticeable; sometimes they blend so subtly into one another that they cannot be observed. Sometimes the pattern is complicated by the child's also developing a crush on a brother or sister or grandparent.

When children reach their teens—or even before—the search for a contemporary of the opposite sex begins. Usu-ally this is preceded by a period when the child sincerely prefers (or pretends to) the members of his own sex. But this mild homosexual interest is not likely to last very long. (Sometimes it is not so mild, lasting well into the teens, but even then in most cases it is outgrown.)

Our society gives its young people a variety of conflicting standards of premarital sexual behavior. Most people and most churches teach that virginity for boys and girls before marriage, no matter how long marriage is postponed, is tremendously valuable. Yet other people and many doctors feel that with our present educational and economic delays to marriage, it is unrealistic to ask young people to wait until their middle or late twenties to make love. Still other people and many parents who believed in virginity and practiced it themselves now look at their children's chances of survival in the atomic age and wonder if they are right to hand on to the children of insecurity the standards of an age of security. Then too, with the advent of the automo-bile, which allows youngsters privacy, and of birth control, which reduces the chances of pregnancy, and of penicillin, which lessens the dread of venereal disease, fear of discovery does not hold youngsters back from making love today as it did in previous generations. Also, as if they needed to be sexually titillated, our young people cannot escape being exposed to suggestive billboards, movies, magazines, radio programs, and book jackets, all contrived by those models of virtue and right-living, their elders.

By and large, the decision about how to behave before marriage is left up to the individual youngster. Promiscuity is frowned on by almost all sources of authority, but if a boy and girl in their twenties (or even late teens) are deeply in love and cannot get married for some time, they may be given contradictory advice. America, perhaps because of our melting-pot of traditions, seems to be currently in a time of transition as to moral standards. In the early part of this century it was an unspeakable disgrace for a young woman to lose her virtue before marriage. During the Jazz

"Mr. Perchmen! I'll see you in church first."

RICHTER © *Collier's*

Age in many circles it was an equal disgrace if she reached her early twenties and had still retained her virtue. We seem to be seeking a middle path between these two extremes which will somehow combine a realistic appraisal of the sexual urge in young people with an allowance of full value for their vulnerability and their idealism. Certainly there is today even less doubt than ever that a close marriage is a rare and wonderful thing, worth long-term effort and sacrifice to achieve. For we not only recognize, as did our forebears, that two people who are happy together have the power to spread happiness far beyond their immediate circle, but we also recognize to an unprecedented degree, because of modern psychiatry, the extent to which a harmonious home is insurance against mental or emotional disturbance in the children. Still the question remains, how can a close marriage best be achieved?

Within marriage itself, the better the sexual adjustment between the partners, the more easily the other adjustments are likely to be made. Good sexual adjustment, however, involves many factors besides the physical. Both partners have carried with them into physical maturity remnants of their early dependent and aggressive urges. Since many of these are unconscious they are less apt to be talked out than acted out, and hurt feelings and disappointment in the partner are often the result.

What happens then depends somewhat on each partner's ability to size up the other's unconscious needs. (This sizing up may be quite unconscious too.) Even the most mature people need a vacation from acting like an adult—and in the privacy of the bedroom they can allow themselves

[79

to be "babied" or to "let off steam" without embarrassment and loss of prestige. But if both partners give in at the same time to their unconscious dependent or aggressive urges, or

"Why don't you ever turn around the way other men do? Do you want people to think I'm married to a piece of wood?"

HOFF © Park East

if one partner gives in to them all the time, the balance necessary to keep the marriage on an even keel may be lacking. The ideal is a seesaw arrangment through which each partner takes turns satisfying the childish needs of the other, while himself remaining temporarily mature enough not to catch these contagious, unconscious emotions.

In the sexual adjustment itself Freud found the chief trouble of the male to be doubts about his masculine prowess and the chief trouble of the female to be concern over her feminine desirability. There is considerable question as to whether this difference between men and women is biologically or culturally based. But there is little question that the role of the woman is to be responsive and of the man to be assertive; if the woman is too directly assertive she may accomplish less than nothing, while if she is desirable and encouraging she may indirectly accomplish everything.

For this reason, admiring oneself (narcissism), although frowned on in men, is encouraged in women. (Freud noted our society's curious indulgence of narcissism if practiced by women or children or cats.) Indeed, it is in the area of self-beautifying more than any other area that women are expected to compete with one another. The adage, "A woman dresses more for other women than for men," has truth to it; but indirectly it contains a compliment to the man in her life. If the small details of a woman's dress (which the man himself may not perceive) are handled to perfection, it may be an unconscious trumpet-call of power from the woman to other women, conveying the idea: "Look what a man I've got (or will get), since nothing is good enough for him but the best."

Yet a woman's feeling that she looks attractive may not be so much the result of what her mirror tells her as of what her man tells her. If he says she is lovely, the chances are she will feel lovely, while if the mirror tells her she is lovely and the man does not, she will probably feel insecure and unlovely despite the outward evidence of her beauty.

"It was sweet of you to notice I'm wearing my hair differently."

COLIN © *Fawcett Publications, Inc.*

With young girls, attractiveness is closely tied in with popularity. The more boys (and even girls) to phone her, the happier she is. Fortunately for girls in our time, the unequal division of good looks by Mother Nature makes less difference than it used to when the only activity open to young ladies was to sit in a swing, trying to look desirable. Today girls can make themselves attractive to boys by being a good sport and by sharing the boy's interests, from bebop to electronics.

On the other hand, girls today with all their cosmetic and educational aids can hardly afford to ignore the lesson taught to their grandmothers—a lesson about the seductive power of the feminine ear. A girl who listens to a boy in such a way that he feels he is quite a fellow will not only encourage him to *be* quite a fellow, but also to be *her* fellow. A girl is proverbially said to "catch" her man, but this catching is done less by rod and gun than by sweet snares that the man may recognize as such but falls into anyway.

Girls early learn to mask their direct aggression when men are around. For women in this world, which is still in many ways a man's world, often "the longest way 'round is the shortest way home." That some women mind having to use methods of indirection may be indicated by the large number who admittedly would prefer to be men, compared with the small number of men who would admittedly prefer to be women. (Almost all little girls, for a while at least, would prefer to be boys, but little boys early repress what desire they have to be girls.)

Yet the women who excel in the indirect approach sometimes grow to enjoy the sense of power they get from influencing their men without the men's suspecting it. These women feel most superior when their men *think* themselves superior. Women in France, for example, refused the franchise for years, each one apparently figuring that the best she could do with her vote if she disagreed with her husband was to cancel his out; whereas with nothing but her feminine helplessness to go on—without that right to vote which would get her husband's back up—she might cajole him into changing his vote, thereby exactly doubling her effectiveness.

"You'll always feel better after a good cry, daughter. It sort of gets things out of your system and also gets things out of your husband."

ROIR © *Collier's*

Just as men have the power to make women proud and secure in their feminine attractiveness, so women have the power to make men feel proud and secure in their virility. Here is the Achilles' heel through which mortal wounds can be inflicted. In fact, it's too easy—easier than taking candy from a baby—to shake a man's faith in his masculine prowess, or a woman's faith in her attractiveness. Perhaps because a man starts out so small compared with his giant father and suffers during early childhood from nightmare terrors of losing what little he has, he needs constant reassurance that he is as good as the next guy, or better, or at least plenty good enough. Some men seek to avoid this fear of inadequacy by acting like Don Juan, and some by remaining bachelors (if they never try to make love, they cannot be accused of failing). Even comfortably married fathers of grown children, when confronted by the waning of physical prowess with age, have been known to fall all over young girls in an attempt to fool themselves, if not the girls, into believing that they are by no means as old as they look.

"Well, I'm disenchanted, too. We're all disenchanted."

THURBER © The New Yorker Magazine, Inc.

So the "war between the sexes" goes on and on, each sex with the power to please the other indescribably, each with

[85

the power to hurt the other unbelievably; each combining a physical maturity, which calls for union of two people by mutual adjustment to the other's needs, with unconscious remnants of the earliest dependent and aggressive urges.

Then on top of these real problems there is superimposed by Tin Pan Alley and our books, magazines, movies, and ads, the romantic myth that for each person there can be but one true love ("Some enchanted evening, when you find your true love . . .") and that when the Right One comes along, there will be only moonlight and roses, nectar and ambrosia. Any problems on the honeymoon? Certainly not. Why, just look at the name: "honey" for sweetness and "moon" for glamor; there is no room there for the fears of inexperienced young men and women, which often lead to impatience, disappointment, and tears. Any unpleasant or boring adjustments to be made? Certainly not. "Forever wilt thou love and she be fair."

In no country but America is this romantic vision believed in so fervidly. For centuries in the Orient marriages have been arranged by parents for children who hardly know one another, with the understanding that if the marriage does not fully engage the attention of the young man, he can have all the concubines he can afford.

In Europe, too, marriages have been arranged by the parents, and love affairs outside marriage, if discreetly handled, have long been the accepted thing for women as well as men, at least in the larger towns. But in America, if the marriage does not automatically turn out to be made in heaven, there is sometimes terrible doubt raised in each partner about his or her adequacy (either as to male prowess or feminine desirability), and this in turn may lead to torturing jealousy. Such jealousy may of course not be recognized by its host for what it is: people seem to be about as

"Thank goodness, you're not insanely jealous, pet!"

PARTCH © *Collier's*

reluctant to admit jealousy in themselves as they are to deny their senses of humor. Jealousy, therefore, is likely to work underground, urging the insecure and despairing partner to seek reassurance outside the marriage, which action in turn might well lead the other partner to feel insecure and jealous and do the same.

Still, all these various kinds of marriage are an improvement over the marriageless primitive societies in which literally no connection was drawn between the making of love and the appearance of a baby nine months later. (Somehow it does seem rather incongruous.) In our system, at least a moderately stable economic, social, and personal framework is provided for children to grow up in. But when modern American parents who are well aware of their parental responsibilities none the less find, in one case out of three, that separation, desertion, or divorce is the only way out of the tension developed in their marriages, the situation might bear some looking into.

To be sure, our present system works wonderfully well in some cases. It is like

> The little girl who had a little curl
> Right in the middle of her forehead.
> When she was good, she was very, very good
> And when she was bad, she was horrid.

But there are not enough of the good cases. No American business would operate by any such slapdash methods; why, then, should our marriages? Might we not instead attempt an impartial auditing in order to gauge where changes might best be made?

One change that cries out to be made, at least from the psychiatric point of view, is to stop thinking that certain parts of the human body are unattractive, if not actually disgusting. If God created us, one might argue against the Victorians, who are we to condemn such essential parts of his creation? As one modern writer has put it, perhaps the worst obscenity of all is to believe and act as if all parts of our loved ones (or ourselves) were not to be loved. Or, to paraphrase Hamlet: "There is nothing [beautiful] or [ugly], but thinking makes it so."

Another change is to stop unconsciously expecting perfection of ourselves or our partner. We may respond if we will to songs about the one preordained and idyllic love, but we need not "buy" this to the point where we are overwhelmingly disappointed when the nuptial sheet is pulled back and we and our partner both turn out to have large, flat feet of clay.

Lastly (although the list could easily be extended) we might try to change the influence of our basic urges on marriage by recognizing them for what they are, admitting their unconscious power over us, and then, after giving the devil his due, continuing to progress beyond them. For, true as it is that we still unconsciously yearn for the passive bliss of infantile dependence, even if this could be fully realized it would no longer be enough. True as it is that we still unconsciously want to strike out at whatever frustrates us, even if this could be fully indulged it would no longer be enough. True as it is that we still unconsciously yearn to feel ourselves petted and cherished, even if we could devote full time to this it would no longer be enough. By the time we are adult, we have developed a need to make others happy, not just to be happy ourselves. The self-absorbed joys of the baby have been to that extent outgrown. Often to the mature man and woman it is not only more blessed to give than to receive but also considerably more fun.

Although psychiatrists have come to this conclusion, it was a minister who described it most memorably. He was distinguishing between lust and love, but what he said applies equally to immaturity and maturity:

> *Lust implies a willingness to destroy the other for the satisfaction of the self, whereas love implies a willingness to destroy the self for the satisfaction of the other.*

When both partners are mature, each caring as much for the other's needs as for his own, the joy that arises is all that the song-writers and ad-men say it is. Furthermore, medical research has recently exploded that ancient, double-standard theory that women must love their lovers in order to be fully satisfied, but that men need not. On the basis of scientifically conducted interviews, doctors now recognize that there is a lack of full satisfaction in the grown man who makes love to a woman he does not really care for. Somehow the human, unlike every other animal, has developed to the point at which really good sex is no longer to be blindly chanced upon, but must first be controlled and then mixed with love and tenderness and then generously shared.

(((III)))

Anxiety

❖❖❖

*Of harmes two, the lesse is for to chese.**

GEOFFREY CHAUCER
Troilus and Criseyde

IT WOULD BE A WHOLE LOT EASIER to describe what our basic urges and feelings don't do than what they do, since their "fine Italian hand" can be traced in everything we think and feel and do from the time we are born until we die. When our basic urges are relatively satisfied, we tend to think more clearly, feel better, and act more reasonably. When, as inevitably happens, they come into active conflict with one another and with the rules of our society, we tend to think more confusedly, feel worse, and behave more irrationally.

It seems unbelievable at first that our basic urges should affect the way we *think*! Surely, when we add one and one, we will find the answer to be two, no matter which of our basic urges is acting up at the time. But what if, when add-

---

* This same idea of choosing the lesser of two evils was also expressed long ago by Thomas a Kempis and Erasmus.

[91

ing one and one, we were driving a car and a child ran across the road? Wouldn't the whole problem, not to speak of the answer, fly right out of our mind? Similarly, if the greatest mathematical genius were sufficiently depressed, he might lose his memory of numbers, or his ability to concentrate on them, or his will to make the effort necessary to add them. Or if, for example, the cause of his depression had been the loss of his lady love, his answer to the question, "What is one and one?" might be a mournful: "It used to be one."

In sum, our basic urges are rather like our need for money: if they are satisfied, we do not have to think about them, but if they are thoroughly frustrated, we may be able to think of little else.

The influence of our basic urges on how we *feel* is sometimes only too evident and sometimes relatively obscure—but whichever it is, one thing we may count on: the intensity of our feeling will not last.* Even the greatest joys and sorrows eventually lose their force. When Heraclitus said that change was the law of the universe, he was not thinking specifically of human feelings, but what he said can be applied to them. A person who maintains one climate of feeling all the time is as unusual as a place where the wind blows only from one direction; both do exist, to be sure, but they are exceptional. It is normal for the winds of our feelings to vary continually—which is one reason why other people find it so hard to gauge their flights by

---

* Only if the feeling remains deeply repressed will it not be influenced by the passage of time. Like a well-preserved mummy, it then tends to remain intact until exposed to light and air.

us. While our changeableness may cause trouble for others, a continued unchangeableness may be a sign of trouble in ourselves; depression or hilarity or apathy lasting unrelievedly over a long period may be a symptom of mental illness.

As for the things we *do*—or, as psychologists say, our behavior patterns—these are affected by our basic urges of the moment and also of the past. Our basic urges start out being the same as other people's, but somehow during our early years they are frustrated or satisfied or redirected in such a way that our actions often end up being quite different from other people's. How does this come about? Is this primarily the effect of heredity or of environment?

No one knows for sure. There is as yet nowhere near enough scientific evidence to say which qualities are inherited and which are learned. (It can be predicted with some accuracy that two blue-eyed parents will have blue-eyed offspring, but it cannot be predicted that two intelligent parents will have intelligent children or that two feebleminded parents will have feebleminded ones. Whereas the pigment of brown eyes is carried by a single gene, something like intelligence depends on a great number of genes.) Even when a child is the spit and image of one parent, there is difficulty in telling whether such traits as tone of voice, motions of body, and expressions of face were developed after he was born or before. All that can be said with certainty is that while we are born equal in the eyes of the law, we are not born identical.

We each start out with a unique constitution in which the same basic urges as other people's are combined in different ways. Then we are affected by an environment that is different from that of all other people. (Even the environments of identical twins are not absolutely identical.)

LIFE'S DARKEST MOMENT

The shock of realizing that nature neglected to provide the puppies with short tails and a fashionable clip.

WEBSTER © *New York Herald Tribune*

What we learn from our environment depends partly on our ability to learn and partly on what we are taught. Psychiatry, which cannot after all do much about heredity, has concentrated on how and what we learn, on the theory that what has been learned can sometimes be unlearned and then relearned—and that although it is impossible to make a silk purse out of a sow's ear, it is possible to return a purse that the environment has caused to look and feel like a sow's ear to its inherent silkiness.

The crucial area of our environment is the home. In a sense we never outgrow what we learned "at mother's knee and other low joints." Mother and father (or their substitutes) are the key figures around whom our basic urges develop, and their approval at first means the difference between life and death, and later between our own satisfaction and dissatisfaction with ourselves. Late into life our peace of mind is connected with parental approval and with the approval of society at large, which unconsciously is accepted as an extension of the parents.

Actually society-at-large is just a fancy name for most-people-near-by, whose values have already come to us built in, so to speak, by way of our parents. For what is done and not done in the home usually reflects what is done and not done outside the home, since our parents, being human, yearn for the approval of *their* parents and most-people-near-by. Occasionally a genius or a disturbed person will fly in the face of society's disapproval, but the rest of us tend to conform, most of the time—at least in the public part of our lives—with the patterns of behavior prevailing where we live.

The advice, "When in Rome do as the Romans do," quoted by Saint Augustine, of all people, is common sense and also an expression of a widely felt impulse in man (perhaps not unrelated to the way animals instinctively develop protective coloration so as to blend in with their fellows and their environment and thus avoid danger). A human being

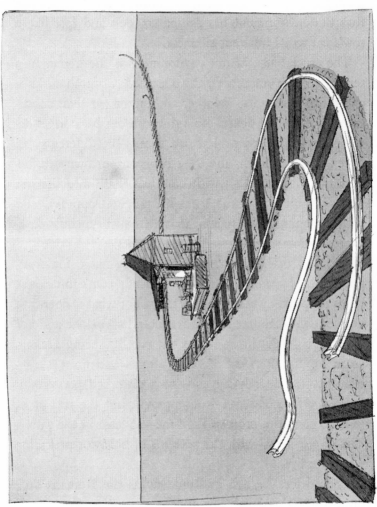

You're a victim of your own environment.

is not, of course, so much a herd animal as a sheep is, but most of us do prefer to be like (or as good as, or better than) other people. Indeed adolescents, who despite their protective coating of know-it-all are more insecure than adults, seem barely able to exist without the latest brand of blue jeans or jazz record that "everyone else" has.

Whereas small children learn what society expects of them through their parents, after starting school they also learn from other children. And this later learning, despite

"Look what I learned in school today, Pop!"

BOLTINOFF © *Collier's*

its sometimes conflicting with what is taught in the home, may well be remembered long after the content of the school's courses has been forgotten.

For some reason, in order for a comparison of ourselves with other people to have emotional impact on us, we must be able to identify ourselves with them. A toddler will look with eyes of worship at a two-year-old who can run, while the fact that majestic grownups can do far more impressive things will leave him cold. A housewife will read with little interest that an heiress has ten mink coats, but if Mrs. Smith down the block starts sporting a beaver, there may be some hoopla. If a stranger wins the Irish Sweepstakes, we will be far less annoyed than if it is someone we know.

Thus we combine a measuring of ourselves according to our parents' specifications with a stacking up of ourselves against the people to whom we feel akin. And during childhood these people are likely to be our brothers or sisters or the kids in our classes. American schools foster this latter kind of self-measurement by giving marks, encouraging competitive sports, and allowing popularity contests. As a result, as children we may strive, at least unconsciously, to be as bright as the brightest in the class, as athletic as the most athletic, as popular as the most popular; and when we fail, as by the nature of competition almost all of us must, we may continue, consciously or unconsciously, to suffer from the sickening feeling that we have not done all that was expected of us.

How, in fact, do we learn what is expected of us? This is the kind of problem to which psychological research in recent years has devoted much attention. The little that is known to date is that the pattern starts very early. When, as babies, we are "good," our parents are pleased and their pleasure is felt as a reward; and when we are "bad," they are displeased and this displeasure is felt as a punishment. Since human beings as well as animals, as many laboratory experiments have verified, have strong tendencies to seek rewards (pleasure) and avoid punishments (pain), there is great incentive to repeat actions that lead to reward and avoid those which lead to punishment. But in addition to the parents

SOGLOW © *The New Yorker Magazine, Inc.*

whom the small child yearns to satisfy (even before schoolmates enter the picture), there are his own basic urges, which he also yearns to satisfy. Very soon he finds that these respective demands may run counter to one another, that the selfsame act that satisfies his urges may frustrate his parents, or vice versa. How is he to choose between them? This bewildering situation which confronts all of us from early childhood to the end of our lives might be set up as follows:

REWARD	PUNISHMENT
An act tends to be repeated if it either	An act tends to be avoided if it either
1. satisfies a basic urge	1. frustrates a basic urge
2. succeeds in its objective	2. fails in its objective
3. is praised by other people.	3. is disapproved by other people.

[99

For example, a child climbs on a chair to reach the cookie box and is caught with crumbs still on his mouth. He has satisfied the basic urge of hunger and has succeeded in his objective (two forms of reward), and yet he is disapproved of by his parent (one form of punishment). (Or an act like retaining virginity, which is rewarded by the approval of society, may eventually be felt as punishment because it frustrates the basic urge of sex.) If the cookie-snitcher was quite young, probably what he learned from his experience was simply not to snitch when parents are around. This sensible solution to his problem (two rewards and no punishments), like the cookies themselves, however, could not last. As he matured, he would find that his parents were *always around*, that their forbidding and their allowing had been gradually incorporated into his very self. If he was lucky, he would find their presence made known by way of the still, small voice of conscience; if unlucky, by way of the mute but powerful billy of the unconscious policeman.

It's natural enough that, since a small child loves and admires his parents above all others, he should absorb their ways of feeling, thinking, and acting above those of all others. "Imitation is the sincerest form of flattery," and is also one of the most important factors in learning. Psychiatrists speak of the unconscious form of imitation as identification, but this is not too different from the childish copy-cat. Of course we also learn by imitation from people other than our parents, and at stages in life other than childhood. People in love are likely to pick up mannerisms from one another and even, if married for a long time, to grow to look alike. And many of us can remember historical or fictional characters whom we tried valiantly to emulate. The line between ourselves and other people is always a fluid one. (Sometimes a state of mind, like panic, will spread faster than any germ.)

"A voice keeps crying, 'No! no! Stinkie!'"

PARTCH © *Collier's*

It is therefore not surprising that when parents are themselves confused and anxious about what is right and wrong, and hold double standards—one for what they say and another for what they do, one for what they do by day and another for what they do by night—and when values of

[101

home and the world outside the home conflict with one another, these various do's and don't's are incorporated into us at an early age. We cannot, after all, sift out only such

"Junior! Will you please stop eating like a horse?"

REA © *Collier's*

standards as are consistent with one another and ignore the rest. For a while, uncritically, we swallow all that is put before us and only later perhaps suffer the pangs of having taken in more than we could digest. By that time we may unconsciously be pulled in so many different directions that, like the rats who are suddenly given electric shocks near the spot where they are accustomed to expect food, we tend to waver, start one way, then reverse ourselves, and feel that no matter what we do we will somehow be in the wrong.

This is a formidable predicament, far worse than being conscious of our temptations, intelligently weighing the rewards and punishments involved, and then deciding to forego, say, the satisfaction of some basic urge. When we make such a conscious choice, we are at least able to feel the reward of knowing that we are doing the right thing; the other way, however, even when we do the right thing we feel no reward, since the feeling of nameless anxiety persists.

We all know the difference between the fear of a definable outer object, like a car bearing down on us, and the anxiety (Freud called it introverted fear) that suddenly wakens us sweating in the night to worry over what we

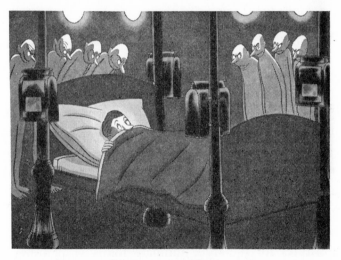

I wrote a stupid letter.

© *Abner Dean*

know to be inconsequentials, or that even in the daytime suddenly drains the joy out of whatever we are doing.

Can we be more precise about this pervasive anxiety?

Perhaps the following division may help to pin down this dread unconscious feeling to which we all at times are subject.

1. *Desperation* and *desolation* are what we feel when our urge toward *dependence* has long been deeply frustrated or repressed, is now being stirred up, and yet is provided with no acceptable outlet.

2. *Fearful* and *threatened* are what we feel when our urge toward *aggression* has long been deeply frustrated or repressed, is now being stirred up, and yet is provided with no acceptable outlet.

3. *Guilt* and *shame* are what we feel when our urge to love and be loved has long been deeply frustrated or repressed, is now being stirred up, and yet is provided with no acceptable outlet.

In other words, these various forms of anxiety may be directly related to our three basic urges, even though what the anxiety focuses upon appears to have no connection with these urges. Furthermore, in view of the unconscious tendencies of tit-for-tat, belief in symbols, imperviousness to reason, and avoidance of pain, it is more than possible that unconsciously we even welcome these three forms of anxiety. Unconsciously we may feel they are appropriate substitutes for the three ultimate forms of punishment which not only have been meted out in primitive societies for the forbidden indulgence of basic urges but also continue to appear in the dreams of normal people and the fantasies of the mentally ill. These three ultimate punishments, which in essence constitute our greatest fears, are:

1. Desertion by the very one (or few) whom we need most.

2. Loss of body integrity (parts of us being cut off or injured).

3. Being cast out by society (all other people).

It has not been conclusively proved, but it is more than likely that: (1) desertion, the retaliatory punishment for our forbidden dependency-urges, is what we are trying to fend off by feeling desolation and desperation; (2) loss of body integrity, the retaliatory punishment for forbidden aggression-urges, is what we are trying to fend off by feeling threatened and fearful; and (3) being cast out, the retaliatory punishment for forbidden urges to love and be loved, is what we are trying to fend off by feeling guilt and shame.

What lends credence to this theory is that all three ultimate punishments, to the child and to the primitive, mean not only pain but death. Then surely the tremendous instinct of self-preservation would be mobilized against them. This instinct, as Harvard's great physiologist, Dr. Walter Cannon, proved through his experiments with animals, always leads to a girding of the body for fight or flight. Both these alternate reactions involve measurable increases of sugar and adrenalin in the bloodstream, heightened breathing and blood pressure, and draining of circulation from the inner organs toward the big muscles necessary for either running or attacking. Do these same physiological reactions occur in human beings faced by the various kinds of pervasive anxiety? They do. When we feel either desperate, threatened, or guilty, our hearts pound, our breath comes fast; in short, we unconsciously react to what is causing these feelings in the same way in which animals (and ourselves too) react to mortal peril.

Unconsciously we fight or flee what is causing these feelings in a number of ways that psychiatrists call the uncon-

"*I can tell you one thing right off—you can't solve your problems by running away.*"

RICHTER © *The New Yorker Magazine, Inc.*

scious defenses. These are made use of by normal people, and often succeed in their aim of making life easier and pleasanter. They also are made use of by mentally ill people, but to such an exaggerated degree that instead of making life easier they tend to make it harder. Like medieval fortresses, these unconscious defenses may become so strong, their walls so thick, their moats so deep, that traffic to and from outer reality becomes limited or completely blocked. It may take a doctor with his armament of knowledge and patience to get through to the person who has unconsciously set up such bristling defenses.

These defenses are quite varied. Some, when we are confronted by their action in other people, amuse us; others annoy us; but all of them share one common denominator: a certain degree of repression. This degree of repression, however, also varies tremendously: in the defense called suppression it is usually very low, while in the one called total forgetting or amnesia it is very high.

Actually the unconscious defenses, several of which are presented below, appear rarely as lone stars but rather in galaxies, and in effect combine many different degrees of consciousness and unconsciousness. All, if watched for, can be spotted in normal daily life, and most of them also appear in exaggerated form in the common mental disorders.

Suppression:
Related to our ability to forget unpleasant things is our conscious refusal to admit they even exist. "Why no," says the child with streaming nose who wants to go to the birthday party, "I don't have a cold." Of course he may be fibbing—but it's also perfectly possible that suppression is

working to prevent him from admitting to himself the possibility that he might have to miss the party.

Suppression differs from repression in that what is repressed cannot be recalled and what is suppressed usually can. People who suppress may say: "I had no idea until it

"Naw, didn't bother me at all!"

MARKOW © *Saturday Evening Post*

was over how frightened I was." But had the experience been repressed, this fright might later neither be recognized nor relieved. Thus suppression accomplishes the same purpose as repression without the latter's potentially painful after-effects. Being a useful and flexible form of defense, it is less likely to appear in mentally ill people (whose unconscious defenses have gone beyond the bounds of usefulness and flexibility) than in normal people.

Forgetting:

Whereas suppression includes *deliberately* putting things out of our awareness, forgetting involves *unconsciously* keeping things out of our awareness, and both differ from repression in that if their subject is forced to our attention we will not deny its existence. Sometimes our forgetting has evident purpose to it and sometimes not. When we

Very bad memory.

© *Abner Dean*

forget the street number of someone's home, it may mean that we don't want to see him or it may mean simply that we have a memory untrained for numbers.

Every neurotic patient at one time or another forgets an appointment with his psychiatrist or arrives so late that half the time is gone. He does not deliberately intend so to waste his money; he thought he wanted treatment, but because the treatment frequently reactivated old, distressing conflicts, he unconsciously protected himself by letting the appointment time go by unnoticed.

The most radical type of forgetting is amnesia. (The amnesia caused by brain injury is the only kind in which unconscious forces are not responsible for what is forgotten.) Its victims are sick people who have forgotten whole sections of their past life. The people and problems forgotten are always found later to be associated with painful unconscious conflicts, and the return of memory is usually accompanied by great anxiety.

Rationalization:

This is giving a reason for some action or attitude on our part which may make perfect sense, but is not the true underlying one. Here the person most likely to be fooled is the rationalizer himself.

An age-old example of rationalization is the fox who could not reach the grapes on the vine and therefore insisted they were sour. Similarly, we all may unconsciously refuse to let ourselves yearn for something patently beyond our reach, and even insist that we would not take it if it were handed to us on a silver platter.

Another example, normal enough but not very sensible, is the person who rapidly loses weight, vomits, and has a severe recurring pain in his stomach, attributing this with great certainty to dyspepsia or change of water. If he were to admit that he ought to see a doctor, he might end up being told what he dreads to hear, and so instead he persuades himself that there is no need for him to see a doctor.

A neurotic patient who was earning virtually nothing, but

to whom owning a car was an extremely important symbol of achievement, bought a brand-new coupé. He sincerely believed that going for a drive each day was necessary to his wife's health. Of course his wife enjoyed the drives, but

"Size sixteen isn't as large as it used to be, is it?"

ROTH © *Saturday Evening Post*

her enjoyment was not so great as her worry about being in debt.

The psychotic person who killed President McKinley was absolutely persuaded that McKinley was scheming to destroy America. Although the sick man hated killing above all else, he felt that it was his duty to assassinate the President in order to save the country.

Isolation:

In times of emergency we sometimes surprise ourselves

"It doesn't take much to collect a crowd in New York."

ADDAMS © *The New Yorker Magazine, Inc.*

by our own aplomb: we have a feeling that this must all be happening to someone other than ourselves. Such detachment is essential to military men who, if they had to feel intimately each soldier's death that resulted from their orders, could never fulfil their job as commanding officers. The surgeon undertaking a difficult operation or the psychiatrist confronted by the agony of a mentally ill person must also employ some isolation in order not to become so emotionally involved with the patient that he cannot do his job.

All of us, at times, rely on the detachment of isolation when we think about our own death or that of the people we love. Moreover, partly because of this ability of ours to disconnect or isolate emotions, and partly because of our highly developed consciousness, we are able to view present, past, and future in such perspective that the importance of even imminent death is dwarfed. Other times of course we feel so frantic at the thought of pain or death that for a while no appeal to objectivity makes any sense emotionally to us.

Most of us seem to shuttle back and forth between a self-oriented world-view and a world-oriented self-view. When we are looking at things one way we are not always able to remember how it felt to look at them the other way. Yet in time we swing back; often many times within a single day.

But with some neurotic and psychotic patients the loss of emotional participation in the patient's own life may last and last, reaching physical peaks where healthy limbs do not react to the pricks of a pin, or psychological peaks where the person can recount the grisliest crimes he has committed without a flicker of emotion.

Displacement:

When we unconsciously switch not our emotions, but the *object* of our emotions, we sometimes experience the relief of discharging these emotions without arousing either the person who originally exacerbated them or our own feelings of anxiety and guilt.

Walloping a ball gets rid of a lot of pent-up aggressive

ADDAMS © *The New Yorker Magazine, Inc.*

and sexual tension. It would be hard to imagine adolescence without the relief of banging things around in sports.

Another normal example of displacement is a matron's sudden decision to houseclean when she is suffering from vague but strong dissatisfactions with her home life. The result may be both a new look in the home and on the face of the relatively satisfied lady. Her husband, however, may then be forced to stop displacing his annoyance with his boss onto the sloppiness of his home, and instead may start kicking the dog. (Sometimes pets fulfill the same function in our homes that the whipping-boy used to in medieval times.)

Psychiatrists are convinced that displacement, among other things, was operating in the seriously sick mind of Hitler when he tried to blame the Jews for all the ills of mankind. Similar forms of displacement can be seen in any mental hospital, where some patients attack anyone who comes near them. Their tremendous hostility against some person once near and dear to them was never admitted to consciousness and cannot now be admitted and is therefore exploding out wildly onto other and quite innocent people.

Projection:

Sometimes we attribute to other people those of our own emotions which we cannot bear to face. While displacement is unconscious switching of the *object* of the emotion, projection is unconscious switching of the *host* of the emotion.

For example, when we do not want to admit hating a person, we may feel sure that he or she hates us. Children, who rarely can admit all their hostile feelings toward their parents, sometimes feel convinced that their parents don't love them despite the most obvious evidence of their parents' affection.

Another normal and in this case valuable example of projection is our readiness to believe that the person we love loves us. Young suitors of coyly cool young ladies might otherwise never get up the nerve to declare themselves.

Sympathy (feeling for others) and empathy (entering

"If you men weren't so stubborn we could be unanimous."

HUFFINE © *Collier's*

into the feelings of others) would probably be impossible without some degree of projection. Closely allied to this is our ability to enjoy plays, movies, and books, where our emotions and those of the protagonists become thoroughly intermingled.

In sick people, a hidden hostility may be projected out onto someone else, and the patient will then fear this person. With a neurotic patient, projection sometimes takes the form of his being afraid to go out of the house alone;

with a psychotic patient, projection sometimes causes terror that "they" are about to get him.

Magic Thinking:

In this scientific age we know perfectly well that magic does not exist, but unconsciously we sometimes still believe in it. Fantasies in which we are the incredible hero help to satisfy our unconscious desire for omnipotence (which probably stems from that earliest experience of believing ourselves to be the whole world) and, if limited, do no harm. Indeed, ambition is based to some extent on the power to daydream and to believe in what looks like the impossible. Certainly too the wonder of being in love in-

"Of course, my secret ambition is to be a surgeon."

KETCHAM © *Collier's*

cludes belief in the magical powers of the beloved. Here too symbolism comes into play. Knights of old went to their death for the glove of a lady. And today lovers may carry the photograph of their beloved next to their heart, feeling comforted just by its presence. Or they may whisper her name over and over, almost as an incantation.

On the other hand, even in normal people magic thinking can bring needless unhappiness. If someone is struck by a falling tree, his perplexity is likely to include: "What did I do to deserve that?" even though he is quite aware that trees do not choose the people on whom to fall. Therefore, besides the bump on the head (based on reality) he may suffer unconscious guilt (based on unreality). From such unconscious guilt (which is tied in with the symbolic and tit-for-tat unconscious tendencies), he may then seek relief through expiatory self-punishment in the form of further mishaps; at least this appears to be one explanation for certain neurotics' getting themselves into endless trouble.

In sick people, neurotic and psychotic, the real may become so blurred with the unreal that nonexistent voices are heard and invisible things or people seen. The world of a psychotic, like the world of a small child, is often peopled by magic forces that no one else can see or hear.

Dreams and Fantasies:

Closely allied to magic thinking when we are awake is the magic thinking when we are asleep. As Plato noticed, "in dreams desire tends to satisfy itself in imagery when the higher faculties no longer inhibit the passions." But even

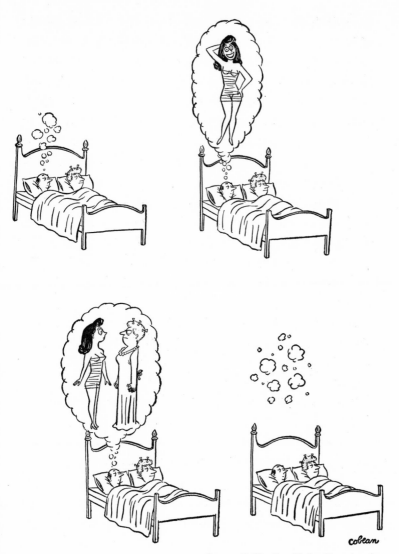

COBEAN © The New Yorker Magazine, Inc.

in dreams, as Freud pointed out, we are subject to our unconscious policeman, whose self-appointed purpose in this instance is to protect our sleep. Were we able to dream our unacceptable feelings in raw undisguised form, these, like our too-vivid nightmares, would wake us up. Therefore, in order for us to stay asleep, our basic urges are forced to appear all dressed up in symbolic costumes, which are sometimes the same as those used by the basic urges of other people, and sometimes entirely personal to us. The ones that are common to many people in many cultures, appearing also in mythology, are: birth symbolized by water, death by departure, father by king or ruler, mother by earth, sex by travel, danger or the male sex by snakes, and the female sex by houses, baskets, and other containers.

In normal people dreams release unconscious tension by synthetically gratifying pleasant wishes or by giving us practice in facing feared situations. What is called "the riddance dream" is our unconscious rehearsal of what we fear might happen or has actually already happened, so that familiarity with it will breed contempt.

Freud called the dream "the royal road to the unconscious," and experts sometimes attain insight into what is bothering us by exploring what lies behind a recurrent dream. The more nonsensical it is, the greater the degree of disguise and therefore, presumably, the greater the importance to us of what is hiding behind it.

The difference between normal people and sick ones is that the sick ones sometimes cannot wake up from their dreams, and continue when awake to talk illogically, with no consideration of space, time, or gravity, and to act as if the symbol were the real thing.

"*You lie!*"
BERENSTAIN © *Fawcett Publications, Inc.*

Denial:

> "*Oh wad some power the giftie gie us
> To see oursels as others see us.*"

The fact is, we can't. The unconscious defense of denial

prevents us from recognizing that other people may think we are no good. Because we do not want to face it, we do not face it, and what is known as the brutal truth consists of facts that are too unpleasant ever to be faced by us unless we are forced to do so. Our insistence on believing the best about ourselves often spreads to include our children, and when someone gives us or them a compliment that we really know to be unrealistic, we go right ahead and believe it anyway. For how can we help having a sneaking suspicion that the nicest things we hear about ourselves and our loved ones have some truth to them?

A mental patient may so strongly deny his own imperfections that he ends up convinced that everyone is out of step but himself and that, for example, in a job at which he fails there must have been a conspiracy against him. Thus, in extreme forms, the defense of denial, like that of projection, may result in violent suspiciousness.

Reaction Formation:

The acting out of the exact opposite of a person's true feelings often takes the form of a thin disguise that fools no one but its wearer. The old maid who looks in terror (real to her) under her bed lest a man be hiding there may unconsciously be suffering from blighted hope rather than from fear; and when someone is saccharine, or unctuous like Uriah Heep, there may be an extreme degree of hidden hostility in him to which we are unconsciously reacting when we hope never to see him again.

Closely allied with reaction formation is overcompensation. After Theodore Roosevelt had been weakened by tuberculosis, he went to such gigantic efforts to make up for his disability that he became a Rough Rider. And Lord Byron, born with a club-foot, became an expert dancer.

An example of reaction formation in a mentally ill per-

I wish it were more comfortable.

© *Abner Dean*

son is the exorbitant affection toward his dogs and cats which was displayed by a cruel, insane murderer.

Regression:

We all at times return briefly to an earlier phase of our development. Dignified matrons can still get the giggles like

SOGLOW © *The New Yorker Magazine, Inc.*

schoolgirls, and grown men can hardly wait to buy electric trains for their sons. Both sexes attend college reunions to wear foolish costumes, to stay up half the night, and to enjoy other forms of behavior they haven't indulged in for years. And many adults, like small children, feel disproportionately pleased or hurt by some small thing another person says or does.

With mentally ill people regression can be so extreme that grown men and women forget how to walk and talk, lie motionless in a fetal position, and play with the products of their own bodies.

Freud spoke of regression as an emotional retiring under (inner) fire to previously held positions. Just as in growing up we make successive steps forward into more mature ways of behaving, so can we unconsciously go backward in times of stress. (Don't we all know adults who feel impelled to suck on a cigarette or pipe when things get tense?) Moreover, it is quite possible that without the human ability to regress, sick people could not be aided so much as they are by psychotherapy. For the helpful transference-relationship depends on the patient's talent for reliving early emotions that consciously he thought he had outgrown.

Sublimation:

This unconscious defense is one of the least understood and most important of all. Somehow, unconsciously, our forbidden urges are washed and combed and transformed into acceptable energies that result in the doing of good to the world at large and also to ourselves. The person with forbidden destructive urges may become a great surgeon; one with forbidden dependency urges may write beautiful

"He held her in his arms and felt the beat of the jungle, the roar of the ocean, the . . ."

LIEBSCHUTZ © *The Saturday Review of Literature*

poetry; one with forbidden sexual curiosities may become a psychiatrist. Without any conscious effort on our part, some of our repressed urges manage to combine and form a steady stream of creative energy which can then rationally be focused on activities we consider worth while. Since society rewards sublimations, the person who is able to sublimate is gratified both by the release of inner tension and also by outer approval. Thus sublimation joins suppression and laughter in being a particularly benign form of unconscious defense, and one to which mental patients rarely have access.

Humor:

Finally we come back to the defense mechanism that this book attempts, to some extent, to mobilize. As Ernst Kris has written: "Under the influence of the comic, we return to the happiness of childhood. We can throw off the fetters of logical thought and revel in a long-forgotten freedom."

Everyone except the very sick has a sense of humor. In some people this may show but rarely, because their repressions are so widespread that the point of any joke can't help landing on a tender area. Or, theoretically, it is possible that a person (like an animal) might have developed so few repressions that there wouldn't be enough unconscious tension in him to erupt into mirth.

Inappropriate laughter, although perfectly normal at times (doesn't everyone at some time get to laughing in church or at school?), may reach such proportions in mentally ill people that it becomes a noticeable symptom. But, by and large, laughter, like sublimation and suppression, is rare in mental institutions.

Some normal people report feeling their lips twitching upward when informed of someone's serious plight. This is probably an example of laughter expressing repressed aggression or of its being a vehicle of unconscious denial, in the sense that if we can laugh about, say, death, we feel it *can't* be true. Similarly, an ugly person will crack jokes about his appearance as if, by laughing about it, he could make it less unattractive to others or, like the clown who laughed to cover heartbreak, keep others from suspecting how terrible is his suffering.

(((**IV**)))

Children

◇◇

Give a little love to a child, and you get a great deal back.

JOHN RUSKIN

How CAN CHILDREN be brought up so that they do not learn to rely too heavily on the less-benign unconscious defenses?

Admittedly, there are few things as boring to people without children as helpful hints on the upbringing of the young; yet there are few things as maddening to people who are concerned about their children as books that insist on the importance of the first years of a child's life and then give no specific suggestions as to how to deal with these. Therefore this chapter is included—but in such a way that it can be skipped without missing anything germane to the later ones. What it attempts is briefly to point out the difference between the necessary parental restricting of the child's basic urges and feelings, on the one hand, and their causing him to repress them, on the other. In the bibliography are listed several of the excellent books that deal in detail with this and other aspects of the whole subject.

Restriction can occur without repression and repression

can occur without restriction. An example of the former is the parental scolding administered to the toddler who ventures off home ground into the street. An example of the latter is the child's witnessing of repeated fights between his parents which arouse his deepest anxiety by calling into question not only their love for each other but also their love for him.

The first experience, which involved a direct restriction of the child's actions, is likely not to be repressed because, rather than arouse the child's anxiety about losing his parents' love, it is tacit evidence of the existence of this love. There may be a few tears or childish imprecations but no possibility of later ill effect. Indeed, sometimes no effect at all: he may wander right back on the street again and have to be scolded again, until in time he figures that the reward involved simply isn't worth the punishment.

The second experience, which involved no restriction of the child's actions may well be repressed because fear of losing the loving interest of his parents raises such apprehension in the small child that his unconscious policeman, in order to protect the conscious self, may promptly ram the whole experience down under the surface of consciousness. Withdrawal of their loving interest is a weapon in the hands of parents which is too sharp to be used more than sparingly, if ever, on a small child. We can safely at times withdraw our approval of his actions; we can safely at times withdraw his privileges or pleasures; we can even safely at times withdraw our patience (sometimes the crosser we get, the more convinced he seems to be that we really care about him); but we cannot safely act like an Indian-giver about our deep interest in him, any more than we can about his very life: he needs to feel that both are, from our point of view, his for keeps.

"Be gentle, yet firm. Remember, you're dealing with a sensitive, high-strung little stinker."

DAY © *Collier's*

And when we think about it, this assurance—and reassurance—of our abiding interest in our child involves no hypocrisy on our part. For despite our child's having it in his or her power to make us happy or sad, proud or ashamed, gleeful or cross, he or she does not have it in his power to make us indifferent. As long as we live, we will probably always care more about him (even though we will not always agree with him) than about almost anyone else in the world. He is and always will be almost as important to us as —or even more so than—we are to ourselves. This doesn't mean that we won't want to wring his neck (as we sometimes want to wring our own), or that we won't be in conflict with him (as we are sometimes in conflict with ourselves)—but it does mean that no matter what other interests we have or how absorbed in them we may seem to be we will drop them in a moment if our child is ill or in some other way really in need of us.

When a child feels secure about both parents' continuing interest and affection he will tend to be less troubled by those three greatest dreads: desertion by the few people he needs most, loss of body integrity, and being cast out by society. As a result, he may be capable of accepting restriction in the area of his three basic urges (dependence, aggression, and love and sex) without unconsciously feeling forced to protect himself by way of repression. Indeed, when we see our child manifesting to an unusual degree one of the three forms of anxiety which accompany repression of the basic urges (desolation and desperation, feeling fearful or threatened, and guilt and shame) we can sometimes figure out which of the three terrible dreads may recently have been activated in him. We can then, by offering him an extra-large dose of parental devotion, perhaps succeed in giving him the fundamental reassurance that he craves but may not know how to ask for.

For example, one cheery little boy of four suddenly became cranky and weepy in the afternoons. He seemed to be sleeping more deeply than usual at nap-time—or at least he woke up later than usual, with flaming cheeks, and it took him almost until supper to stop rubbing his eyes and acting so grouchy that his younger brother and older sister refused to play with him. A parental talk with his nursery-school

"*Sure, Ralph Thompson eats, but his case is different—he's afraid of his father.*"

TABER © *Saturday Evening Post*

teacher brought forth no clues: at school he was independent, friendly, co-operative, and seemed to enjoy all the activities except rest-time. Finally one day he mentioned to

132]

his mother that he always dreamed that someone was chasing him and was going to cut off his head. She paid little attention except to say that people didn't get their heads cut off any more. Afterwards she wondered if he had been listening to scary radio-programs, but on investigation found that he was actually shunning these when his sister turned them on.

Nothing much happened for a week or so. Then one afternoon he complained that he had been dreaming that someone was trying to cut off his thumb. The mother vaguely remembered having heard somewhere that small children feared having parts of their bodies cut off and so, mostly on hunch, she put her arm around him and said that she would see to it that nobody ever cut anything off him and that his Daddy would protect him too. The little boy musingly repeated after her: "Daddy won't let anyone hurt me," and she found herself saying with considerable fervor that Daddy would kill anyone who tried to hurt his boy.

The youngster blinked, smiled, squared his shoulders and marched out of the room. It was as if Atlas' load had been lifted off his back. Soon he was heard singing to himself, as he hadn't for months, and the hectic flush on his cheeks at nap-time recurred only a few more times before it disappeared. The little boy had not known what was bothering him—and the mother had not really known either—but somehow he had managed to communicate enough of his anxiety for her to sense that what he needed was extra reassurance about the continuing devotion of both parents.

Perhaps his problem had to do with unconscious hostility toward his father; perhaps not. At certain ages, as Dr. Anna

Freud and Dr. Gesell have shown, particular fears as well as generalized nightmares are more likely to occur than at other ages. But the main thing about this little boy was that

"If you didn't bring anything, why did you come home?"

MACE © *The American Legion Magazine*

with the support of both parents he was able to solve in its early stages some kind of emotional conflict of which he was unaware except through the suffering it was causing him. Of course it is also possible that in time, even without the mother's extra reassurance (which presumably wouldn't have had the effect it did, had the father, in reality, not been interested in and fond of his son), the little boy might have outgrown his unconscious anxiety in that mysterious and seemingly abrupt way that children sometimes manage to outgrow what troubles them.

One of the most baffling things about children is the way they combine with their unbelievable degree of tenderness an equally unbelievable degree of toughness. During the last war the experiences that children went through with no apparent ill effect are staggering to the imagination. Children do not need to be handled with kid gloves all the time; indeed, sometimes when they manage to irritate us to the point where we say things better left unsaid, they don't even have the grace to appear perturbed. It is as if they could drink in through their pores our deep and abiding interest, and brush off as unimportant whatever they heckle us into saying to the contrary.

One can still hear today in public parks and conveyances the three most dread forms of punishment voiced by parents in the form of threats: "I'll go off and leave you if you don't come right now"; or: "If you don't stop sucking your thumb, I'll cut it off"; or: "No one is ever going to love you if you do that." Yet the children don't seem unduly fazed. Presumably they are so sure of the affection of the crochety parent that they simply don't believe he or she would really hurt them or allow them to be hurt. Still, since psychoanalysis of troubled adults has so often dredged up similar past experiences that the patient had repressed because they were so unbearable, it seems safer for parents to dream up some different kind of threat.

Just as important as reassuring our child that our affectionate interest can withstand any naughtiness of action on his part is our reassurance that our affectionate interest can withstand any forbidden thoughts or feelings on his part. Sometimes, actually, a child is more alarmed by his own thoughts and feelings than by his actions, because the former range so much further into forbidden territory. Probably one of the most worrisome comments the post-Victorians made to their children (perhaps because it had been made to them) was: "How can you *think* such a thing?" As we know now, people can't help the thoughts that pop into their minds, and if any one of these is then emphasized by another person, it tends, like the white elephant, to haunt its host all the more.

The counterpart of that old remark was: "How can you say such a thing to your own *mother?*" Yet if one can't say things to one's own mother, whom is one ever going to be able to say them to? And furthermore, why should a child be made to feel unnatural, leprous, unlovable, when he has already exercised huge self-control in confining himself to *saying* what he thinks, rather than acting it out?

We today encourage children to be honest with themselves and with us about their own basic urges and feelings, by letting them know that we can accept these even though we may not like them. We do not, however, allow all these urges and feelings to be acted out. This makes sense not only from the point of view of the society that forbids such acts, but also from the point of view of the child itself. For example, many doctors may feel that if a child is allowed to strike his parent in anger, too much anxiety for the young personality to bear may be aroused by his succeeding in potentially destroying the very person whose loving presence he so deeply craves. (In *Little Men* Louisa May Alcott poignantly described the shattering feelings of the quite-big boy whose punishment was to have to strike the hand of his beloved Professor Baer six times with a ruler.) Thus we sometimes end up being kinder to our child if we restrict his actions than if we permit him to act out what he feels and then be forced to repress the whole experience because it was too excruciating to bear.

Yet when we restrict a child we are likely to arouse his hostility. What can we do to help him before such hostility mounts to the point where talking it out is no longer enough of a release and he either has to repress it as being too threatening or explode it into some forbidden action? Here is where any and all of the arts and crafts come in handy. In some way, not yet well understood, the destructive and creative impulses in human beings are closely linked: the child who has fun making a mud pie has just as much fun squashing it; the older child who enjoys building a tower of blocks enjoys toppling it, too; the writer who is in love with the sound of his own words also glories in cutting and slashing them (in order, he hopes, to heighten the effect of the few that are left).

In some seriously ill people, schizophrenics in particular, this destructive-creative linkage is more than ever apparent. Van Gogh, within a short period of time, cut off his ear, offered it to a woman in a brothel, and then painted what is often considered his best self-portrait, in which attention is focused on the bandage around where his ear used to be. Research is now going on to ascertain how our destructive energies are and can more effectively be sublimated into constructive activities.

Surely, if all the pencil-scrawls, the crayonings, the finger-painted whorls, and the filled-in coloring books currently in production by the American young were laid end to end,

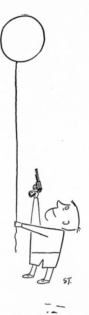

STEINBERG © *The New Yorker Magazine, Inc.*

they would stretch around Betelgeuse. Add to them the dancing, the singing, the instrument-playing, the reading, writing, sports, dramatics, sculpture, and carpentry in which our children also engage, and we may be right in thinking that in some ways at least we are doing better by the next generation than did the Victorians. For, while they were content to teach their children to block their basic urges, we are trying to teach ours to divert them creatively. This, combined with the honesty we are trying to help them develop as to what their own basic urges consist of, may result in their using suppression rather than repression, and using sublimation and laughter rather than, say, too much fantasy or projection or denial or rationalization.

How, in effect, do we encourage our children to laugh? The main way, of course, is by helping them to be happy and healthy. Another way is by laughing ourselves. Anxious, overserious parents may follow the directions in the child-rearing books in greater detail, but they may not end up doing so much for their children as do the parents who drop the book in order to go out and have fun with the kids. Still another way is by providing the child with small contemporaries (or brothers or sisters) who can join with him in his rather primitive attempts at humor. When the giggling starts, particularly in relation to parts of the body and fixtures of the bathroom, the hear-no-evil monkey is perhaps the one for parents to emulate, particularly if their sensitivities are at all on the delicate side.

Still another way is to let the child spend time alone with adult relatives and friends who love him but feel so little direct responsibility for him that they are more liable than we to be amused by his antics. This amusement of theirs in turn tends to increase the child's self-confidence and light-heartedness—until he becomes such an unregenerate show-off that we are forced to slap him down.

Then finally there is the gurgle, almost indistinguishable from a laugh, that comes from the child who feels himself learning a new skill, whether "pumping" on a swing or drawing a house that looks, of all things, like a house. This we can encourage by abetting our child to do things in which he has a fair chance of succeeding, rather than, as some toy-salesmen perennially would have us do, providing him with equipment for which he is far too young.

Our child's ability to please us not only is one of his own greatest sources of pleasure but also tends to build his confidence and courage. Therefore it is better, when we evaluate his accomplishments, to compare them not with those of some more-gifted child or with those of some preconceived ideal of the perfect child but with what our own little dumbbell could do last year. For, when we pay attention to his accomplishments and are openly pleased with him, the lift he gets encourages him to try new things. But if we are indifferent or openly displeased, he may feel so discouraged or afraid of failing that he won't try new things. Parental comparisons and other forms of competition in childhood may act as a spur or a drag. To the child with inner confidence and ability to succeed, competition can keep him on his toes. But to a child without basic inner confidence or ability to succeed, competition may be a source of sickening despair.

Where does this so-important inner confidence come from? To some extent from the child's inborn constitution and from other factors over which we have no control; but to some extent also from his having experienced an affectionate parental restriction of his actions, instead of either an unloving parental restriction or no restriction at all. The degree of loving restriction that helps to build the child's inner confidence has a wide range of variation between what is called leniency and strictness. Moreover, that degree of leniency or strictness which is chosen by any one parent will tend to vary further as applied to different children in the same family and also as applied to the same child at different ages. Some children seem to need far more than do other children the kind of security that comes from being ringed around by parental do's and don't's; and any one child will vary in a zigzag but generally downward trend in the amount of parental restriction he needs from early childhood to late adolescence. Thus, although parents shouldn't permit on one day what they have just forbidden the day before (unless there is good reason for such a change), that much-advised parental consistency in the handling of children is not exactly easy of attainment. At one end of the scale is the need of the adolescent (for all he may gripe about it) for some parental limitation of his freedom, in order perhaps to reinforce an excellent decision of his own which he has not yet the maturity or inner strength to maintain unaided. At the other end of the scale is the toddler who is already so utterly frustrated by being smaller and clumsier than everybody else that parents may help him more by ignoring some unimportant peccadillo than by interfering and thus adding a final straw of frustration to the already overburdened little camel.

If there is anything we have learned about small children, it is that frustration is probably more deeply upsetting to them than it will ever be again. Having neither any perspective nor any inner resources to speak of, children are rarely able to bear without tears or tantrums even the postponement of a fundamental satisfaction, let alone its complete denial. As a matter of fact, one criterion of maturity is the ability to withstand temporary frustration without blowing an emotional gasket. During infancy and early childhood, therefore, the direct frustration of basic urges should probably be kept to a minimum, and when such frustration is unavoidable, as sometimes happens, it should probably be sugar-coated by some extra reassurance as to our devotion and interest.

Since the three basic urges develop from infancy on at different paces, they are here presented separately, although, of course, in real life they are inextricably commingled and often cannot be handled separately:

The urge of *dependence* should probably be as thoroughly satisfied during the first years of life as is possible without completely unraveling the parents. Perhaps because being held and fed is the only way a baby can perceive the love of his parents, he may unconsciously interpret the lack of such holding and feeding as a lack of love. In any event, we know it is tremendously painful to the baby not to be fed when he is hungry or held when he is forlorn. Even in later childhood, when we sense that either the drooping lower lip or the snarling upper lip is caused by feelings of desolation or desperation, we may find that a parental hand on the shoulder or kiss dropped on the top of the head brings forth a deep childish sigh of relief, a dazzling smile, or a sudden upsurge of energy.

Closely tied to dependency problems are eating problems. Here doctors believe that the less of an issue parents make about whether the child eats or not, the more likely nature is to take its course and in time build the child's appetite. After all, when the instinct for survival is the parents' ally, they can afford to sit back and let the child work out his own pattern of eating within the framework of the wholesome and appetizing foods they offer him. (The same kind of sitting back by parents is also advised in relation to the cleanliness training of the child; in time he will want to be clean and dry, partly because it is more comfortable and partly because the people he admires always are that way.)

When the basic urge of *aggression* begins to develop, the

"Are you the young man that bit my daughter?"

THURBER © *The New Yorker Magazine, Inc.*

baby tends more and more to wean himself from the warm encircling arms and stand on his own widely spaced feet. Of course, when he is sick or troubled, he will want to touch home base again, but the intervals between such returns will tend to lengthen, and should not be discouraged by parents from so lengthening.

While doctors believe that direct satisfaction of the dependency urge in infancy may lead to less tension in this area later, they believe that the aggressive urge should quite early be parentally redirected. Removing breakable objects from the living-room will save future heartache on the part of both parent and child—as will providing ample opportunities for childish play with water, sand, mud, sticks; for climbing, swinging, jumping, shrieking; for energetic but not violently hostile interchanges with small contemporaries and large pets (small pets may not survive the "loving" to which they are subjected). Most of these activities will unfortunately play havoc with the child's clothing and the family furnishings, not to mention the parents' equanimity, but these, in the last analysis, are all replaceable and well worth expending in the effort to help the child drain off his tremendous aggressive energies in a way that is emotionally and physically beneficial to him and does no real harm to anyone else.

For a youngster to learn to share toys with other children is difficult and takes time and repeated adult encouragement and example. When the other child involved happens also to be a brother or sister, the problem is intensified. Sometimes it helps for parents to explain that although a particular toy can be held by only one person at a time, the love of a grownup can be held by many people at a time: that like the milk of a cow (or any other mammal-mother) the more it is drawn upon, the more there is to draw upon.

As for the urge of *love and sex*, the more warmhearted affection a child gets from both parents, not despite his being a boy or girl, but because he is whichever he happens to be, the better off he is. On the other hand, because there probably is in all of us some completely unconscious seductiveness toward members of the opposite sex, it is just as well for parents not to be entirely uninhibited about showing their affection through physical contact. Some parents kiss their children on the lips, some share their beds with the children; in themselves these actions need not be harmful to the child—and may even be very precious. But in some children similar personal contacts have been found to have become a little too precious, with the result that the child

"They belong to my sister."

GORDIN (SIVIC) © *Argosy*

suffered vague but painful unconscious guilt or shame. Although an infant can take—and even needs—a great deal of cuddling close to the uncovered portions of his parent's neck and arms, the older child needs this cuddling to be gradually cut down.

As for the child's handling himself, this, like most matters connected with sex, is probably best approached by parents giving, in as matter-of-fact a way as they can, those truths which the child seems ready to understand. When a toddler, usually at the least suitable moment (from his parents' point of view), suddenly starts clutching himself, we can tell him that this is something which well-brought-up people simply don't do in public (the truth). But we should

"You've got a 50–50 chance. If you're a boy you stay—if you're a girl you go."

HELLE © *Saturday Evening Post*

not tell him that this is something which well-brought-up people *never* do (the untruth, since masturbation has been found to be an almost universal practice during some period of childhood or adolescence).

Where we run into particular difficulty is in figuring out what, if anything, to say to the older child who may or may not be indulging secretly to a limited extent. (If an older child indulges openly or excessively, this is usually a sign that professional help is needed: sometimes a slight infection may be causing itching that brings the child's hands to that area; other times an emotional distress may be causing undue reliance on this infantile form of satisfaction; still other times the doctor may find nothing more complicated than underpants or pajama bottoms that have become too tight; but it is always well to make sure.)

Certainly the child himself is unlikely ever to bring up the subject. Should we mention it and perhaps, like the oversolicitous mother who warned her children: "Don't put beans up your noses," suggest a diversion that the child might not have thought of at that stage in his development? Or should we, in this instance, continue not to know what our child is doing? The arguments for the latter course of action are several:

First, there is no danger that our child will suffer physical harm from a limited amount of masturbation. The old-wives' tales about its causing blindness, insanity, bad complexion, and what not have been scientifically disproved. Secondly, there is some danger that an emotionally charged parental forbidding of the child's touching himself may result in such repression of the child's sexual urge that when grown up he may not be able to function normally in this respect. Thirdly, there is a comparable danger that the child may develop terrible self-loathing and lack of confidence when he finds he cannot (when half-asleep) completely keep himself from doing what he has been so forcefully told is unnatural and vile. Fourthly, we may be sure that even though we never say a word about it our child will pick up the idea that this is an activity about which the people he admires are not exactly enthusiastic. Fifthly, if we have never frightened our child about masturbation he may feel free to tell us when and if little school friends make physical advances (which little school friends sometimes do), thus enabling us to protect him by insisting on supervision when the children visit each other's houses or even by cutting out the visits for a while.

The last argument—perhaps most controversial of all—is that through allowing our child to keep a few deep dark secrets from us we may be reinforcing his grasp on reality and diminishing his unconscious tendency to believe in symbols and magic and other forms of unreality. As was noted in the second chapter, the baby starts out thinking that he is the whole world—and then that the mother or the bottle are a part of himself. So agonizing to him is the truth that he is separate and helpless, that he may for a long time be unable to accept it. Furthermore there appears to him to be evidence on the other side: that this is not the truth. After all, when he wants food or warmth, his parents usually provide it without his having to tell them. Perhaps his wishes are so potent that they can cause events; perhaps his parents are still so much a part of him that by looking in his eyes they can read his inmost thoughts. Undoubtedly he doesn't think it out very clearly; but such feelings, in vestigial form, are often mentioned by normal children. And many an emotionally disturbed child (and adult too) still insists that his wishes have magical power to influence events, or that his parents (or "they") know so well what he secretly thinks that, as a result of their familiarity with his unspoken hostility, they cannot possibly love him or keep from wanting (on a tit-for-tat basis) to hurt him.

What a child apparently does not realize for years is that,

although his parents in some ways know more about him than he knows about himself, no human being will know all about him ever. His is an essential privacy that starts at conception and continues throughout life. And his gradual but thorough realization of its existence, despite any apparent evidence to the contrary, may well be one of the foundations of his sense of dignity and unique worth.

Parents therefore do their child a favor by refusing to pretend (as did many Victorians) that they are omniscient. Certainly they must guide their child in the direction that they think is right: a mealy-mouthed lack of parental conviction about important decisions is not going to be of much use to the child. But when the parents' decision has to do with something either so controversial that they don't know what to say, or so likely to be outgrown by the child that their saying nothing does no harm, perhaps the best course is for them to allow the child to keep secret whatever he does—or doesn't do—in this connection.

Some day, perhaps, there may be definite patterns established in this most important realm, the field of child development, or preventive psychiatry. Meanwhile the professionals, for all their new clinical discoveries, are still rather like Hansel taking Gretel (the parents) by the hand when both are lost in the woods. On some occasions Hansel can spot landmarks invisible to Gretel which indicate the path to follow; but on other occasions he, like Gretel, may have to fall back on hunch and hope and patient trial-and-error before finding a path that despite all detours leads in the right direction.

(((V)))

Normal and Abnormal People

◇◇◇

Existence is irrational and so is the love of it; and while we exist, we cannot escape either.

GEORGE SANTAYANA

DR. THOMAS FRENCH tells the story of the two men sitting in a restaurant on a hot summer's day who were arguing about how to distinguish abnormal from normal people. One man insisted that he could spot an abnormal person a mile away. "Why look," he said, "at that girl over there by the window banging herself on the forehead. Clearly she's off her rocker." The other man looked and had to admit that the girl's behavior did seem peculiar. The discussion and the meal having ended, the two men rose. On their way out they passed the table of the lady who was still busily slapping. It was only as they came abreast of her that they saw the big black fly buzzing around her head.

One thing about normality, like happiness, is that although we can't define it we know we want it. But unlike happiness we don't necessarily know when we've got it. How do we judge when we are normal? By comparing ourselves

150]

to other people. But how do we know *they* are normal? By whether their actions seem appropriate to their situation. But how do we know what their real situation is? As in the

"See a good psychiatrist—for what?"

DAY © *United Newspapers Magazine Corp.*

example of the lady and the fly, it is not easy to judge from any distance what someone's outer situation is, and even harder to judge the inner one.

Yet most of us tend to hold up the normal as an ideal, strenuously objecting to any implication that we or our children might be abnormal. At the same time we do not mind being told that we are above-normal although, strictly speaking, above-normal *is* abnormal since the most common definition of normal is average or conventional. Thus, by the definition of normal as average, it is normal to have cavities in our teeth because most people do. But by the definition of normal as model, it is abnormal to have cavities since the model person would not—and in this sense of the word there can be no such thing as above-normal.

[151

Is it not a curious semantic position we are in, not wanting to be abnormal (different from other people), yet wanting to be abnormal (better than other people), since this is closer to normal (model)?

Actually, by any definition of normal, it is impossible to be normal all the time. For one thing, the values of our society conflict so with one another that we often cannot distinguish between the paths we are expected to follow. We are admonished from the pulpits of segregated churches to love all human beings as brothers. Should we or should

"*Please, John—people are staring.*"

PARTCH © *Fawcett Publications, Inc.*

we not bring a Negro friend, or, being Negro, insist on going to such a church? Millions of Americans say yes; millions say no.

For another thing, there are few feelings or acts, whether reminiscent of the beast or of the angel, in which it is not normal to indulge *every now and then*. Other people may be alarmed by the intensity or inappropriateness of such feelings or acts on our part, but we need not be alarmed. For, as psychiatry has discovered, continual optimum performance of the emotions is no more possible of achievement than continual optimum performance of the body. Just as we all occasionally pick up some physical ailment, whether a trick knee or a headache or a sniffle, so, for no evident reason, do we feel or express unreasonable anger, apathy, worry, or depression. But as long as these do not color our whole life and instead allow us to work and play and get along with people, they are perfectly normal. Indeed, psychiatry describes them as "the normal deviation from the normal" and fully expects people to be "subject to change without notice."

Outwardly the final test of normality and abnormality is whether society insists that treatment be applied. When a person is seriously ill, the question of treatment is not left up to him: society, if necessary, cancels all his civil liberties in order to enforce hospitalization. Conversely, in the milder forms of mental illness and in the early forms of serious illness, and even in the brief vacations from normality which all of us occasionally may go off on, the question of treatment is left up to the individual. Whether he decides to seek help or not depends on how much he is suffering, how much he is causing others to suffer, how near at hand there is professional help that he can afford, and how much he is prejudiced against seeking it. (A thirty-five-year-old patient this year was told by his well-educated, well-traveled, well-heeled parents that they would rather see him "dead than going to a psychiatrist.")

Inwardly the test of normality and abnormality might be the application of that synonym of normality, "well balanced," to the three determinants of action listed in the third chapter: reward through satisfaction of basic urges and feelings, success in what we attempt, and approval of other people. If some act of ours satisfies more of these than it frustrates, and we therefore repeat it, this can be called normal. But if some act of ours seriously frustrates most of these, and we none the less keep repeating it, this can be called abnormal. For example, the fanatic (compulsive) handwasher neither satisfies the repressed feelings that are straining to become conscious, nor does he succeed in symbolically cleansing himself of the unconscious guilt that hagrides him, nor does he win the approval of other people; and yet he continues his washing until, in some cases, the skin comes right off his hands.

This factor of repetition is crucial to the concept of normality. No single act, in itself, can be called normal or abnormal: we must know the whole context of the person and the values of his world before we can attempt judgment. If we come upon a man washing his hands when they are dirty, we think nothing of it; if we come upon him washing his hands when they are clean, we may think he is extra-fastidious, but nothing more; if we come upon him a couple of times washing his hands when they are clean but we know that he has just been admitted to some organization whose initiation ceremony involves absurd actions, we also think nothing of it. Only when we know that he repeats this handwashing regardless of circumstances—and indeed cannot be stopped from repeating it, no matter how inappropriate it may be, do we have grounds for believing him abnormal.

All circumstances change—with rather frightening rapidity at times—and the normal thing is, within reason, to adapt ourselves as best we can to the changes. Normality is no continuing state of bliss: there is nothing static about it. And the person who remains rigidly the same, always predictable, is less likely either to achieve satisfaction of his basic urges, or to reach long-run success, or—and this does seem rather unfair—to be rewarded by the approval of other people, than the person who learns and grows. For, even when such consistent behavior on his part is desirable and worthy, we tend to shun him as a goody-good.

The concept of goody-good is a particularly difficult one for children to grasp. Their parents, who have constantly been telling them to be good, are now condemning someone for being too good. But how can anyone be too good? Undoubtedly they can't if they remain warm and sympathetic, which is, however, what the rigidly virtuous person fails to do.

The two most truly virtuous persons who ever lived (in the eyes of their respective millions of followers over the centuries) were anything but goody-goods. Moses was kept from entering the Promised Land because of having "rebelled against [the] commandment [of God] in the desert of Zin," and Jesus let fly with "a scourge of small cords" at the money-changers in the Temple. Moreover, when the self-righteous scribes and Pharisees reminded Jesus that the penalty for the woman taken in adultery was to be stoned to death, he turned on them, saying: "He that is without sin

Accumulated virtue.

© Abner Dean

among you, let him first cast a stone at her," while the woman was gently admonished: "Go, and sin no more."

Moses and Jesus did not ask perfection of people: they asked them to love one another. And love includes forgiveness. Certainly the people they surrounded themselves with were far from perfect. There were instances in both their lives when the men they depended on most let them down at a crucial moment—and yet Moses spared the life of Aaron who had helped fashion the golden calf, and Jesus, after Peter had just denied him for the third time, only "turned and looked upon Peter."

Perfection within himself is not only impossible of attainment by imperfect man, but is not even particularly enjoyable to him in the areas where it is possible. The inspired architect of the Parthenon deliberately placed his columns at uneven intervals lest mathematical exactness offend the human eye. The great poets have always varied the length and rhythm of their lines lest these sound like jingles. And Sir Francis Bacon's statement, "There is no exquisite beauty without some strangeness in the proportion," is not too different from the old Chinese proverb: "Your virtues annoy your friends; it is your imperfections that endear you to them."

Somehow it makes us uncomfortable when something or someone is too good to be true. And in the case of a human being, we may be right to be leery of him since, when basic urges are too tightly repressed, they may explode dangerously. Such a person may end up doing great good in the world or great harm—but in either event, like the dog-paddling swimmer, he is probably not much of a companion to the people around him.

One of the hallmarks of the fanatically or abnormally good person is that he doesn't seem to get any kick out of being good. For the rest of us virtue sometimes *is* its own reward. We get a warm feeling when we are able to help someone in need, we exult when we rise above temptation, we relax after a job well done. These are the rewards of the conscious conscience. But for the person completely dominated by the unconscious policeman, the only reward seems to be a momentary relief from the billy's belaboring.

On the other hand, the people who give in to their basic urges all the time are not normal either. "Man," as Bernard Shaw described him, "the inventor of the rack, the stake, the gallows, the electric chair, of sword and gun and poison gas," can hardly afford to yield to his basic urges at all times. For better or for worse, we have developed a state of civilization which demands that people (and nations) control their urges for the sake of others.

No longer today do we need to devote most of our time to keeping warm and fed and protected from wild animals. No longer in order to communicate with one another must we walk long distances. Within a few moments we can be in touch with people at the other end of the world—and through the written word we are in contact with people of the past, the present, and, we hope, the future. For more people than ever before, life is easier and richer than ever before. (Theoretically, man could go back to living like an animal, but having developed such intelligence, sensitivity, and conscience as he has, it is hard to imagine his again being happy in such a primitive and lonely state, if indeed he ever was.)

But the price of living in our civilization is that we must suffer the unconscious tension brought on by the conflict between its rules and our own basic urges. Dr. Lawrence

Kubie has referred to human beings as being like automobiles starting off down the road of life. Within each is a tankful of potentially explosive but essential gasoline: the basic urges and feelings. Without the gasoline we would never get started or keep going. Also essential to our survival and that of the other cars are the brakes, which, if reasonably applied (conscience), serve to keep us on the road, but which if jammed (unconscious policeman), may wear out the tires, slow up the car, and possibly upset it.

If a car with jammed brakes happens to remain throughout life in something like a school zone, where the speed limit is only ten miles an hour, its inability to speed up may never come to anyone's attention. But on a parkway this same car would be in the way of other drivers, and if confronted by a high hill might never get any further.

The conscious self or driver cannot see under the hood while he is moving, but he can watch the dashboard indicators, the road signs, the other cars, and adjust his accelerator and brakes accordingly. If he hears a knocking in the motor he will, unless he is afraid or in too much of a hurry, stop to have it checked. In our time there are more mechanics (psychiatrists) available than ever before. Or if the car is well made and the trouble is slight, an average gas-station attendant (friend, minister, family doctor, psychiatric social-worker, or public-health nurse) may be able to fix it.

Some cars seem built to operate best on country lanes, others in the hurly-burly of city traffic. But all need gentle handling during the first thousand miles (childhood), and all can be forced beyond their limits into some kind of breakdown if the road is rough enough (during the war some experiences were so dreadful that even the strongest soldiers succumbed to emotional or physical breakdown). It is also true of all cars that when the road is wide and smooth, drivers who start out with the basic minimum equipment can safely stay in the right lane and be approved by the other drivers. But when the road gets rugged, with bumps and curves and one stoplight saying stop and another saying go, it's hard to avoid an accident.

When a car is balky, one thing the mechanic may do, besides inevitably taking longer than one thinks he should, is try to clear the gas line against clogging (by too much repressed material), and at the same time to adjust the carburetor so that gas doesn't flow too freely either.

But except in the extreme (abnormal) cases of damage, it is hard to tell when the car needs a thorough overhauling and when, if allowed to run a bit longer on a slightly better road, the trouble might disappear of itself. Just as normality cannot be pinned down, so in the less-extreme cases abnormality cannot either. The difference between normal and abnormal is like the differences between shades of gray.* Subtly they blend into one another, and a great deal of further scientific research is necessary before any clear distinction can be made between the early stages of serious mental illness and the chronic forms of mild mental illness, and the normal deviations from the normal.

Furthermore, whatever shade of gray a person happens to be at one time is likely to darken or lighten quite suddenly. Human beings are not like the old silent-movie hero or vil-

---

* *Shades of Gray* was the title of a first-rate Army movie on mental health. See Bibliography for other good movies in this field.

lain whose behavior was always pure white or pure black. Still, over the long haul, there have been found groups of people whose patterns and ranges of variation are similar, and whose basic emotional problems are often similar, too. To make communication between doctors easier, labels have been applied (many by Dr. Emil Kraepelin) to these various groups of people.

The darkest shades, the extreme forms of mental illness, which are clearly recognizable when fully developed, are called by the man on the street "insane," "crazy," or "loony." These are known to the doctors as the psychoses, which include schizophrenia; severe depressions, sometimes with manic interludes; and certain disorders due to damage to the brain—the organic psychoses. In all of these the patient loses touch with reality, and his ability or desire to cope with the world is impaired.

No patient is considerate enough, however, to fit neatly under any one of the doctors' classifications all the time: a schizophrenic may exhibit depressive tendencies, or vice versa. But by and large the distinctive symptoms of schizophrenia are withdrawal and loss of contact with people, the symptoms of manic depression are wild mood-swings, and the symptoms of physical damage to the brain are notable defects in memory, thinking, and judgment.

Many of the less-extreme cases of mental or emotional disturbance, often accompanied by physical symptoms, are not recognized as such by the man on the street. He tends to call the sufferer a jerk or an odd duck, or a poor miserable son of a gun. These disturbances are known to the doctors as the neuroses, and include hysterical conversions, ob-

Everyone must have a label.

© Abner Dean

sessions, compulsions, phobias, and milder depressions.

Another type of disturbed person is dismissed by the man on the street as an impossible character, a stinker, a louse, or a no-good guy. These people are called by the doctors in the extreme cases "antisocial personalities" (formerly known as psychopaths) and in the milder cases "character-neurotics." Such people are technically neither normal, neurotic, nor psychotic. They know the difference between right and wrong but they seem incapable of caring one way or the other. They are afflicted by an apparent atrophy of the conscious and unconscious conscience.

The difference between the normal person and the neurotic or the character-neurotic is only one of degree. All of us have neurotic moments: we check and recheck to determine if the oven has been turned off and still worry that gas is escaping, or are unable to go off on a carefully planned trip without a heart-jump of terror that something has been left behind. All of us also have character-neurotic moments: we are awakened for the tenth time in one night by our child's crying; we know that he may need us but for the moment we cannot generate the energy to give a darn. (The difference between the normal person *when awake* and the psychotic or the antisocial personality is more than just a difference of degree. We are aware of reality, intellectually and emotionally, and they are not. On the other hand, even when awake we have psychotic or antisocial moments, as when we are temporarily "beside ourselves" with rage.)

But for the normal person these moments of being neurotic or character-neurotic do not last and last. We can do all kinds of fool things—but then later we realize their foolishness and try to make amends. We are not continually, as John Dollard has characterized the neurotic, "emotionally stupid" and driven to "chronic repetitive maladjustment." We are not continually either overaggressive or

MODELL © *The New Yorker Magazine, Inc.*

overpassive, overimpulsive or overinhibited, anxious, humorless, egocentric, and impossible for people to get along with.

Hard as it is to be friends with a truly neurotic person, it is even harder being one. Perhaps the only way we can imagine the intensity of neurotic suffering is to remember the few worst moments of our lives and picture these being endlessly prolonged. As a character in an Arthur Koestler novel who has been through the worst physical tortures comes to realize, "the hardest sentences are those which people inflict on themselves for imaginary sins."

What are these sins? Many of us arrive at adulthood with feelings of unworthiness far greater than would be warranted by the candy-snitching, hooky-playing, and other mischief we can remember about ourselves. Sometimes we feel so unlovable that we marvel how anyone stands us. Yet we have *done* nothing terrible, only perhaps long ago *wished* that we might. And since in childhood the line between reality and unreality is so fluid, a wish may be felt to be a substitute for the deed.

Having once, perhaps quite unconsciously, wished that a beloved brother or parent would drop dead, we may years later (because of unconscious momentum) still feel like a murderer and be stricken with guilt and fearfulness when that person does die. Consciously we know that rather than cause the death we did everything in our power to prevent it; but because this old aggressive wish was kept by the unconscious policeman from ever reaching our awareness, we cannot even now consciously get hold of it in order to deal with it in an adult and reasonable manner.

The people who not only wish to, but actually perform, acts that are forbidden we call criminals. These people often combine the emotional disorders of the neurotic or character-neurotic (and in extreme cases, the antisocial personality) with a social and economic background that rewards breaking the law more than adhering to it. If a youngster is brought up in a slum area where decent people don't get enough to eat, and gamblers, robbers, and murderers drive fancy cars and live on steak, the reward-and-punishment learning process may well lead him into a life of crime.

Just what constitutes a crime is not always easy to pin down. A person from an upper social level who drinks too much and behaves boisterously at his club may be laughed

"My big regret is that I didn't start earlier. I'da been out by now."

DAY © *The New Yorker Magazine, Inc.*

at in a tolerant boys-will-be-boys way. But someone from a lower social level who indulges in identical behavior at the local saloon may find that the cops are called and he is booked for disorderly conduct.

Many people who land in jail are found to suffer from intellectual stupidity: their I.Q.'s are low. But even more frequently they are found to suffer from emotional stupidity. They seem unbelievably careless of other people's feelings and property, and also of their own future feelings and freedom. How else explain not only the often pointless wastage and cruelty, but also the incriminating fingerprints and footprints that are so frequently left by otherwise intelligent criminals? It is almost as if, accidentally on purpose, they wanted to get caught in order to exchange the agony of their intangible self-punishment for society's tangible and comparatively bearable punishment of a prison term. Since most children learn early that after punishment comes forgiveness, even hardened criminals may unconsciously hope that through serving time they may achieve some expiation for the unconscious sins that date from their childhood and that may or may not in reality ever have been perpetrated.

One of the most distressing aspects of deep, unconscious suffering, whether it leads to acts that society does not approve (neurotic) or does not tolerate (criminal), is the danger of its adversely affecting the sufferer's children. As C. Macfie Campbell has said: "The family is the unit dominated by its sickest member." In this sense the Biblical threat about "visiting the iniquity of the fathers upon the children, and upon the children's children, unto the third and to the fourth generation" is often distressingly borne out, even though what corresponds to the old "iniquity" is often not the sufferer's own fault, nor even within his power, unaided, to change.

A child may react to the suffering of his parent by becoming overly docile or overly rebellious. And such a pattern of extreme behavior often continues into his adulthood. The child of an overly anxious parent might, through identification, become overly anxious himself, or he might, through reaction-formation, turn into a reckless daredevil, or he might do any number of other things—useful or harmful—to prove to himself that there was no cause for his parent to be so anxious as far as *he* was concerned. Either way, it seems harder for him to strike that balance between the extremes which we call normality than it is for the child whose parents have been fairly well balanced themselves.

But until scientific research succeeds far better than it yet has in discovering the factors that, in combination with the environment, underlie mental health and illness, there is no reason for parents to take on themselves full blame for their child's maladjustment, or full credit for his successful adjustment. Nor can the child completely blame or thank himself either. Those things in life over which we have little or no control are far more numerous than those we do control. In addition to the constitutional factors that influence a person's mental health and illness there are many important environmental ones as well. Some of these are: the era into which a person is born; his family's social and economic and educational background (a professor's son who hates books and likes to work with his hands might have been far better off if born into a farming family); whether he is born in the Orient or the Occident, in a dictatorship or a democracy; and whether during some crucial moment in his emotional development he happens upon a parent or grandparent or teacher or friend who perhaps quite unconsciously gives him the inward bolstering he temporarily needs.

Furthermore, as one of the most recent studies of child psychoanalysis concludes: "We have come to understand

"The usual things that happen to every child . . . frightened by a lion at three . . . captured by the Ubangis when I was . . ."

Wiseman © *Fawcett Publications, Inc.*

the extent to which conflict, danger and defense are part and parcel of normal development . . . as essential and necessary concomitants of growing up." No human being can become mature if swathed in cotton wool: we have to learn to take the bumps and bruises along with the joys.

And sometimes the same kind of damaging (traumatic) experience that has been found to underlie the symptoms of mentally ill people has also been found in the childhoods of normal people, who, if anything, have been strengthened by being forced to summon their resources against it.

Just how such healthy adjustment is made, no one knows. Somehow, like an oyster dealing with an irritating grain of sand which has penetrated its shell, we manage to coat these painful experiences over and over again until sometimes a pearl (a work of art or other unusual accomplishment) may result. Other times we manage to dissolve or digest the irritants. Either process takes time—and time is on our side. Thus both are quite different from the process of repression, on which time has no effect.

Another area where more research is needed before we really know what we are talking about is the connection between physical and mental illness. We know that there are often emotional factors in physical illness and often physical factors in mental illness, but which is the cart and which is the horse we do not know.

Modern comprehensive medicine is currently being taught on the theory that in addition to the biological factors in illness there are psychological and social ones as well. Where, the doctor asks himself, does this illness fit into the whole life of the patient? What does it mean to him in terms of his responsibilities, his hopes, his fears? We all know how going to bed with a juicy cold can be more of a vacation than our real vacation. No one bothers us—indeed, people stay away from us if possible—and we are not expected to fulfill any economic, social, or sexual responsibilities. This does not mean that each time we sneeze there must be some hidden significance—but it does mean that

"What do you mean, you don't feel well. You're on your feet, aren't you?"

REA © *Fawcett Publications, Inc.*

if a young lady repeatedly gets ill just before each scheduled wedding day, the young man may be quite right in wondering whether she really wants to get married.

The parts of the body which most frequently serve as symbolic channels for expressing unconscious conflicts are the stomach (ulcers), the intestines (colitis), the skin (certain allergies and eczemas), and the sex organs (impotence, frigidity). Other possibly psychosomatic ailments are high blood pressure, asthma, and headaches. These, like the behavior disorders that until recently had not been attributed even in part to emotional disturbance, cannot inevitably be traced back to the unsolved conflicts of childhood—but in many cases they have been so traced.

For example, the people who knew Jim said he was the picture of health. He was big, dark-haired, muscular, ruddy-skinned. No one but his family knew that he suffered from excruciating headaches—"as if the top of my head were coming off"—and even they did not know how frequently these were recurring and how close he came to "blacking out" when they were at their worst.

The headaches ceased completely while Jim was in the army. When the war was over, Jim came home to a good and responsible job from which he was able to save a fair amount of money. He was hail-fellow-well-met, popular, and no one seemed to notice that he hadn't any close friend. It made him nervous, he later told the doctor, to be alone with one person, except for the girl he wanted to marry.

Jim, at twenty-nine, had not yet told his mother and father he was engaged. His father, a successful furniture-manufacturer, had recently met with business reverses and was forced to ask Jim for a loan. He was a stern man who had punished Jim severely as a child, rarely if ever showing the boy any affection. The mother had been ailing all her life and, since the time he was little, Jim had helped take care of her. She often said: "I don't know what I'd do without you," and while Jim was in the Service she had been severely ill.

One night after going to the movies with his girl, Jim was driving home alone, worrying about whether to lend his savings to his father or use them to get married on. He felt one of his headaches coming and then to his horror thought he saw an old man step off the curb in front of his car. He jammed on the brakes, but to no avail.

The next thing Jim knew he was in a mental hospital. The police, summoned by the burglar alarm in a commercial garage, had arrived to find him wandering aimlessly about with his shoes off. He had broken in by smashing a window and his hands were bleeding. His car was neatly parked outside. There was no report of any old man having been injured in that neighborhood.

For the first days Jim was incoherent, weepy, and almost blinded by the headaches for which careful physical examination showed no organic cause. Pain-killing drugs alleviated them only a little. After psychiatric treatment got under way—Jim was soon able to continue with it on an "outpatient" rather than an "inmate" basis—the headaches began to disappear. What came out in the course of months was that Jim had unconsciously been suffering deep guilt for his long-repressed aggressive feelings against his father.

Jim's fantasy of hurting an old man (a common symbol for father) was one of the first hints that led the doctor to explore such a possibility. Later Jim's mother, when questioned, remembered that Jim as a baby, after being punished by his father, used to bang his head against the crib for what seemed like hours. He also occasionally had resorted to head-banging during the course of her rigid and early attempts at cleanliness training. As she explained, she was the kind of person who "always wanted things just so" and "couldn't bear any kind of a mess."

[173

Jim had always looked up to his successful father and wanted to be like him (he was well on his way to being equally successful in business), but at the same time he re-

"He's an odd case. His amnesia makes him forget he's got insomnia, so he sleeps like a log."

HOFF © *Park East*

sented his father's cold, unbending attitude toward him and his mother. Some of this hostility was conscious—although Jim had never breathed a word of it to anyone—but the greater part was not. It was the repressed part that was violently stirred by the father's sudden reversal of role, now being on his knees to Jim, so to speak, in a way that the helpless and infuriated little boy must often have wishfully pictured. Here at last was Jim's chance to get back at his father for what must have seemed to the child acts of deliberate cruelty. Yet how could he, a grown man, kick someone who was down, particularly the father whom he had always admired? So intense and painful were these conflicting feelings, so close perhaps to erupting into consciousness and from there into action, that Jim couldn't stand it another minute; he lost all consciousness of his past urges, of his present problem, and even, for a while, of his own identity.

Promptly Jim's repressed aggression exploded against the window of the garage. This, like the many other petty crimes performed by amnesia victims, probably served also as a relief, in the sense that he could now be punished for something other than what he unconsciously had wished to do, and perhaps thereby win forgiveness.

Farfetched? Indeed it is. The unconscious *is* farfetched when observed in the cold, clear light of reason. But the fact is that two years of psychiatric treatment succeeded in alleviating Jim's headaches completely. Coincidence? It's possible, of course, but not probable. For, carefully documented, there exist thousands of other cases like it.

The case of Mary was like Jim's, in that her trouble also was the kind that people do not ordinarily recognize as being emotionally based. While Jim, until his attack of amnesia, had expressed his repressed conflicts mainly through the physical symptom of headaches, Mary expressed hers through obnoxious behavior as well as through physical symptoms.

Mary's first years had been happy. Her jolly father worked little and had lots of time to take the little girl around with him. But suddenly, when Mary was four years old, he disappeared, and Mary was left alone with her strict, hard-working mother. During Mary's adolescence she was not even allowed out on a double date, let alone a twosome.

"Yours is a common enough personality problem, Mr. Rankley—you're obnoxious."

GOLDSTEIN © Saturday Evening Post

Her mother subsequently married twice more and Mary never got along with her stepfathers.

After Mary was graduated from secretarial school, she started earning her own money and living her own life. Within the next few years she lived with many men but found satisfaction with none. After becoming pregnant, she married a soldier, but when the baby was born her promiscuous behavior started up again. She made her husband, her mother, and her stepfather miserable by her goings-on, but most of all she made herself miserable. There was no pleasure for her in submitting to men she cared nothing about, yet she kept right on doing it. Within a year, she had lost her husband, several promising jobs as secretary (she had a high I.Q.), was barely on speaking terms with her mother, and at the time of being hospitalized was about to be evicted from her rooming-house because of the disturbances she had caused.

More than anything she wanted to be a good mother. She loved her child and was willing to do anything for him. But it seemed to her that the harder she tried, the less she succeeded. She felt dead-tired all the time, had recurrent pains in her stomach, and couldn't keep herself from being snappish with the baby. She seriously wondered whether he wouldn't be better off if she killed herself. Yet if she did, he would go to her mother. Mary's feelings toward her mother were very mixed. She cringed at her mother's disapproval of her; yet, on her own side, she disapproved strongly of her mother's repeated ventures into matrimony. She hated to doom her baby to a childhood like her own— yet how was she to take proper care of him if she kept feeling as awful as she did and doing the awful things she did?

Mary was brought to the hospital having taken an overdose of sleeping pills. It was relatively easy to save her life physically; but how to save it emotionally?

After a few weeks of quiet, hospital life,* combined with talking to the psychiatrist every day, Mary found herself somewhat more at peace. The doctor was not like anyone

---

* Which included encouragement to eat, sleep and exercise regularly and to engage in occupational and recreational therapy.

she had ever known. All he seemed to care about was how she *felt* in connection with what she had done; not whether this had been right or wrong.

How *had* she felt? She couldn't rightly tell. What had been leading her to throw herself into the arms of man after man, only to freeze up as soon as any of them became ardent? What was she trying to accomplish, luring them on, then discarding them? Who had ever done such a thing to her? Had someone once made her love him more than anything in the world, and then cast her aside? Was it further possible that the feelings she was currently experiencing toward the doctor, of adoration because of his understanding attitude, and of resentment because he cared nothing about leaving her at the end of the treatment hour, were a revival of what she had once felt toward her father? Could it be true, as the doctor suggested, that her desertion of the lovers after arousing their affection was caused by an unconscious symbolic seeking of her father partly in order to punish him? Much of this stuff was way over her head; all she knew was that for some reason she was feeling better than she had in years, eating better since the pains in her stomach were gone, sleeping better, and feeling more confident that she and her little son would make out, if need be, without help from anybody.

When Mary's doctor went into the Service, she promptly became ill again. (Unconsciously this seemed to her like a repetition of the old desertion by her father.) But with the help of another doctor she soon recovered the ground she had lost. When she left the hospital, continuing to see the doctor twice a week on an outpatient basis, she found to her surprise that she no longer even felt attracted to casual male acquaintances. She knew that the three men, her father and the two doctors, for whom she now recognized her own deep affection and gratitude, could never be hers. What she wanted was not some cheap substitute but a lasting relationship. What she was looking for was a gentle, understanding man whom she could respect, who would love her and the child, and with whom she could build a real home. For this she was willing to wait a long time.

Mary, when last heard from, had moved with her child to a new city and was holding down the same job she had had for more than a year. She had not yet found her dream man, but in many ways she had found herself.

Sexual maladjustments, whether in the form of promiscuity, homosexuality, frigidity, or impotence, frequently accompany emotional disorders. However, just what a sexual maladjustment consists of is not always simple to define. Sexual practices that are frowned on in our society have at different times and places been approved. To the ancient Greeks, love of man for man was held as being higher than love of man for woman. And some of our practices, such as kissing on the lips, are thought to be disgusting by the Eskimos and people of certain other cultures.

Since the essential purpose of sexual relations is to express love and lead to procreation, the practices that cannot possibly lead to this end might well be called unnatural, in that they are not according to nature's evident intent. On the other hand, Kinsey's research showed that in a far higher proportion of the population than anyone might have suspected there are no holds barred in love-play preceding union. Secretly, too, what are termed sexual deviations have been indulged in occasionally by a large enough proportion of American males for this to be classed as average if not normal behavior. (Over eighty per cent were found to have experimented with homosexuality.) Here too the shades-of-gray concept applies. An occasional wild oat does not mean abnormality—although continued compulsive promiscuity or overt homosexuality does. It is always the repetition and continuance of failure in one of the big areas of life, sexual as well as otherwise, that points to the existence of emotional disturbance.

If someone appears to be hounded by tough luck, or if he repeatedly enjoys ill health, this may be accidental or it may not. If we are struck by a hit-and-run driver, chances are that from our point of view it was a true accident. But if this particular driver had already hit several other people, chances are that from his point of view it was not a true accident. Sometimes "the fault, dear Brutus, is not in our stars, but in ourselves. . . ." Several new terms have come into use to describe the people who keep bumping into things or in other ways injuring themselves. Accident-proneness refers to those who are constantly getting bruised or cut or broken. Larval suicide refers both to repeated accidents and to chronic illnesses. Both are believed frequently to stem from unconscious guilt and resulting self-punishment in hopes of symbolic expiation.

There is, after all, a limit to the number of different ways we can suffer at the same time. An earache coming when our tooth is already aching hurts less than if it comes when we are feeling fine. Similarly, when we are already punishing ourselves inwardly, a new illness or accident may bother us but little, and may even so distract us from the old nagging unease that we don't want to lose this welcome distraction by recovering from it. Other times a change of pain is felt as a relief. As Karl Menninger pointed out in his book, *Man Against Himself*, there are a multitude of ways in which our tendency toward self-punishment may manifest itself, the ultimate one of course being self-inflicted death.

Deliberate suicide is known to occur in man and the lemming, with a few cases having been reliably observed in dogs. It is an act obviously against nature's intent, and modern doctors believe that anyone who commits suicide, except

STEINBERG © *The New Yorker Magazine, Inc.*

in unusual outer circumstances, such as impending torture, is emotionally disturbed at the time. When we read in the paper about someone killing himself because of business failure or disappointment in love, this is likely to be the surface rather than the underlying reason.

Sometimes a person tries to kill himself in an unconscious attempt to punish other people as well as himself. Like the small child running away from home, he may be trying to make his parents sorry. Or he may be trying to atone for the utter failure that his unconscious policeman keeps making him feel he is. Some mentally ill persons are convinced that they are the worst persons who ever lived, worse than Nero and Judas combined.

One reason for keeping certain mental patients in hospitals is to prevent them from damaging themselves or other people. Schizophrenics and severely depressed patients may seek escape from their intense suffering through death. In the manic stage, too, there is danger that the patient in his agitation may do himself harm.

The shades-of-gray concept applies particularly to depression. All of us get blue at times for no apparent reason. But this is not abnormal. It would be abnormal if we didn't. Human beings are such incredibly complex and finely geared creatures that it is amazing we get out of order as little as we do. The normal person's feeling of wanting to go out in the garden and eat worms usually passes off within a day or week. But a severely depressed person may not bother to get out of bed or even to eat for months and years at a time, having to be fed intravenously to be kept alive.

Among the people who face repeated depression, as well as many other problems, are the old. Death stares them in the face; they feel they have nothing to look forward to.

Their job is over. They are no longer needed. Younger people are bored by their repeated references to the past—and the friends who shared that past are mostly gone.

What to do about our aging population is a problem to

"I'd have called long before this, Gladys, but you know how things keep coming up—the Johnstown Flood, The Spanish American War, The Chicago Fire. . . ."

CAPLAN © *Saturday Evening Post*

be attacked by the young and hale as well as the old. We might well put far more money and thought than we do into figuring out how we can better employ the experience and patience of old people. Adult education flourishes in some localities. Others have old people's clubs. Still others have proxy-grandparent arrangements, enabling the children who need love and the old people who need to give love to

[*183*

get together. But in most places old people are doomed to inactivity, with all the heartache to themselves and waste to society which this entails.

We need not go so far as the Chinese did in setting up age as a prime prerequisite of wisdom, but at the same time our accent on youth need not deprive us of the experience and wisdom of our citizens who are finally dry behind the ears. An active mind in advancing years can be of inestimable value to the aging person himself and also to his family and his world. If he feels not only that his life was worth living but that it still *is* worth living, this attitude on his part may spread, as by osmosis, to his family circle and far beyond, helping to combat the depression and sense of purposelessness which, in our time, frequently beset those in the middle or even at the beginning of the ladder of age.

In certain ways the needs of the extremely old and the extremely young are similar. Both need physical check-ups more often than do those in the prime of life. Both have great need to feel secure and protected (dependent). Both, delighted to feel useful, will gladly fulfill small tasks, but if taxed beyond their strength may retire into balkiness. Eventually senility may affect the brain and nervous system in the same way that some organic illnesses do. A new branch of medicine called gerontology or geriatrics is concerned specifically with the problems of aging.

When the blood vessels harden in the brain and the cells degenerate, then memory, language, and reasoning power are impaired. The person, being unable to use past experience to solve current problems, is likely to panic at the slightest adverse circumstance. For him the best thing is an unchanging friendly environment where he can be with others like himself. The setting up of special colonies for senile people is something to which modern welfare-specialists, both private and public, might give even more consideration than they already do.

In many ways the needs of senile people are like those of the feebleminded who make up the lowest (intelligence-wise) two per cent of the population. Both, as long as they can be useful, are best off living in their own homes. Indeed a great deal of the world's most boring and unpleasant work is done by people with low I.Q.'s. When helped to adjust to their menial jobs, they can be both useful and content. But when caring for them becomes an unbearable strain on their families, they are better off in institutions.

Like senility, in that it also may involve a return to extreme dependence, is alcoholism. Normal people can take a drink or let it alone: drinking falls well within the range of their conscious will-power. But some people have a curious affinity for alcohol. A few drinks for them may start an unbreakable habit. Behind alcoholism often lies the same kind of repressed conflict that bedevils other neurotic sufferers. But even when these conflicts are satisfactorily resolved the ex-alcoholic will not be able to drink socially. He must never drink at all lest the old affinity for alcohol lead him again to drink too much.

Alcohol in large doses acts as a depressant. (In small doses, to a limited extent, it is a stimulant too.) But it is felt more as a stimulant because one of the first things it depresses (lessens the action of) is the part of the brain which has evolved most recently and appears to be responsi-

[185

ble for the function of the unconscious policeman and the conscious conscience. We then get a sense of release, of:

"Do you have far to crawl, Mr. Rushton?"

RICHTER © *Collier's*

"Well, I'm not as bad a guy as I had thought—or perhaps neither is he, or she over there." The old saying, *In vino veritas*, shows that long ago it was recognized that when repressions are released by alcohol the speech or action may reflect our most fundamental feelings.

When an alcoholic has been in an extreme stage of intoxication for some time, psychotic conditions may develop. The patient loses touch with reality. He sees nonexistent, terrifying objects and hears inaudible voices. His judgment, intelligence, and memory may become permanently impaired. Alcoholism, like other forms of addiction, may result in the person's suffering from malnutrition, not in the sense of calories, since alcohol has plenty of these, but in the sense of vitamins and minerals, which alcohol lacks and the drinker usually has no appetite to seek elsewhere.

Before starting to cure an alcoholic or drug addict or sexual deviant, some caution is necessary. The patient's particular abnormal form of adjustment may be the best one he is capable of making. If the doctor blindly charges ahead and removes it, even more serious symptoms may arise. Here again the judgment by doctors trained in modern comprehensive medicine is important. What does this patient's form of maladjustment do to help him? If he weren't a relatively harmless alcoholic, might he develop into a sicker person? Here the needs both of the individual and of society need to be taken into account.

Useful work is being done by Alcoholics Anonymous, which leaves the pace of cure almost entirely up to each individual member. AA has succeeded in putting great numbers of formerly hopeless drunks back into circulation, including many who had reached the psychotic condition called DT's (delirium tremens).

Drug addiction is much like alcohol addiction, only worse. The symptoms are more severe, and the underlying maladjustments are also likely to be more severe. Tightened federal narcotic-laws have greatly cut down the number of cases of morphine, heroin, and cocaine addiction. In some people barbiturates (ordinary sleeping-pills), if taken in large doses, can cause a jag instead of drowsiness. These people feel blissful, free from anxiety, and the more often they feel this way, the more they want to, until their whole lives become centered on procuring the pills. For drug addicts, successful treatment can only occur in a hospital.

When a person starts behaving in a very queer way, statistically the chances are that he is suffering from schizophrenia (the name roughly translates as split personality).

"You said a moment ago that everybody you look at seems to be a rabbit. Now just what do you mean by that, Mrs. Sprague?"

THURBER © *The New Yorker Magazine, Inc.*

This disease, of which the causes are still unknown, fills a quarter of the hospital beds in this country, not just mental-hospital beds but all hospital beds.

Heredity is believed to play a small role in schizophrenia —but just what this is no one yet knows. Unknown organic disorders of the brain are also in some cases believed to play a role. Today psychiatry feels that in many cases of schizophrenia unconscious conflict can be discerned, just as in neurosis.

The schizophrenic person tends to feel withdrawn, as if the world outside were fading away and as if he had become flattened out, shallow, hollow. Some patients become agitated, others become mute. Sometimes they feel persecuted (paranoia) and sometimes they have delusions of grandeur (megalomania). Sometimes their rational faculties return, but in an irrational context. During the war, one patient whose violence caused him to be isolated was found to have bitten himself until he bled, and then to have written all over the walls of his room with his blood: "Buy War Bonds."

Schizophrenia is the disease formerly called dementia præcox. The name was changed because the "præcox" implied youthfulness in the sufferer and this has been found not necessarily to be the case. Today for schizophrenic patients the outlook for a return to normal living is better than it ever has been, particularly if the disease is treated in its early stages. Psychotherapy, in some cases psychoanalysis, group therapy, certain organic therapies such as shock treatment and lobotomy (see next chapter), and a well-planned activities program in a modern mental hospital are potent aids in the psychiatrist's effort to cure this severe mental illness. But a great deal of research will be necessary before it can be said that we have made more than a good beginning.

(((VI)))

The Psychiatrist

◇◇

A patient should look on his psychiatrist more as a beacon than as a wheelbarrow.

REX LARDNER
The New York Post

PSYCHIATRY, the branch of medicine concerned with mental illness, is practiced by doctors. A psychiatrist is by definition an M.D. with many years of intensive post-medical-school training. His approach to helping a "mental" patient may be by way of the patient's body (as in prescribing rest, exercise, baths, drugs, or operations on the brain), or by way of the patient's emotions (as in helping to dispel some of his conscious or unconscious anxiety and changing his ways of life), or, as often happens, by both.

Psychiatrists are not all psychoanalysts, but all psychoanalysts with an M.D. degree are psychiatrists. Psychoanalysis, in other words, is a branch of psychiatry (which is a branch of medicine). Psychoanalysis is a specialized treatment directed toward a thorough emotional re-education of the patient, and is practiced only by people who have them-

selves been analyzed. Most of these people are also M.D.'s
—although a few laymen are recognized as analysts, having
of course been carefully instructed when to call in a medical

"But, Mrs. Wells, I'm your friend—I want to help you."

KING © *Saturday Evening Post*

doctor. Furthermore, the word "psychoanalysis," in addition to meaning a form of therapy which is useful particularly in *treating neurotic people*, also means a theory

(Freud's) and a method of observation developed out of this theory, which are useful in *understanding all people*, normal and psychotic as well as neurotic.

Then, as if to make things as complicated as possible, another form of psychiatric treatment, called "psychotherapy," has recently evolved, and is practiced by those professionals, whether psychiatrists or other physicians or psychologists or psychiatric social-workers, who have thoroughly acquainted themselves with its principles. Some of these principles are based on psychoanalysis; others are borrowed from the old-family-doctor approach of giving the patient an emotional boost through providing needed encouragement, advice, or other support. Actually psychotherapy is not unlike the "casework" of social workers and the "counseling" of psychologists. It differs from psychoanalysis primarily in that its goal, like that of most branches of medicine, is the removal of symptoms rather than the fundamental re-education of the patient. And it differs from psychiatry proper in that no organic treatment, such as, for example, insulin therapy, is ever included.

Each of the three forms of treatment has its uses just as the full-course dinner, the special diet, and the between-meal snack do, and it often takes a trained specialist to recommend which is best suited to the illness and to the capacity for recovery of a particular patient.

All the specialists involved are also expected to know something about cultural anthropology and sociology, so that they can judge which of their patient's odd-seeming thoughts, feelings, and actions are the result of the teachings of his culture and which come from his own unique development. For example, if a patient from an intellectual background avoids everything highbrow, this may indicate rebellion on his part, or some kind of emotional block; while if a patient from a rural low-income background avoids everything highbrow, he is simply following the mores prevailing among the people with whom he has grown up. Since so much of what we think, feel, and do is a result of what we have learned, it is essential that the doctor who wants to help us relearn should know what our particular cultural background was likely to have taught us.

The ideal psychiatrist would be a warm and intelligent person, with a good marriage of his or her own, blessed, if possible, with children. He or she would have been given thorough technical training at a good medical school, and would have picked up a broad cultural viewpoint. For a doctor to be helpful to patients, he must be able to combine common sense (developed through his own living) with uncommon sense (technical training in diagnosis and treatment of mental illness); both are essential. As Dr. Alan Gregg has said, psychiatrists do not, after all, want to be like the plumber who, when called in to fix a leaky drain, ended up tearing the whole kitchen apart and saying to the aghast housewife: "Madam, common sense is a gift of God and all I've had is a technical education."

Psychiatrists do not, however, have to be paragons in order to be able to assist their patients. Often they themselves, having suffered some neurotic disability, have been helped by treatment and, through this experience, have augmented their ability to help people with a similar problem. If, on the other hand, the psychiatrist's disability is not really overcome, he may be unable to assist patients in this particular problem, though he may still be able to assist patients in other problems.

One of the chief reasons for the training analysis of young psychiatrists is to give them insight into their own personal repressions and emotional blocks, so that they can overcome these if possible or, if they cannot overcome them, so that they can at least allow for them. Even the psychiatrists who have not themselves been analyzed usually gain enough insight from their intensive study of Freud's psychoanalytic concepts (upon which this book is largely based) to recognize their own weakest points and thereby avoid taking on patients whose weaknesses are identical with their own.

Everybody, the psychiatrist included, is bound to grow up with a certain amount of emotional astigmatism. We tend not to see the faults of those we love (including ourselves) or the virtues of those we hate (sometimes including ourselves). And to add to the blurring, this love and hatred are often, because of our ambivalence, focused on the same person. So, rather than expecting psychiatrists to see all things accurately, our motto might be: "Among the blind, the one-eyed are king."

One-eyed or not, a serious complaint that can be registered against psychiatrists is that there are not enough of them. There are only six thousand members of the American Psychiatric Association, and there are five hundred thousand psychotics in our mental hospitals. This averages out to over eighty psychotic patients per doctor, and there are very many more neurotics. Grisly as it seems, as many people land in mental hospitals every year as register for college. This lack of psychiatrists constitutes a severe challenge for teachers of psychiatry. Somehow they must manage to train many more psychiatrists, particularly for teaching, research, and work in clinics and hospitals. Since public funds have become available through the Mental Health Act, there is hope that this will be done in the not too distant future.

Among the few psychiatrists there are, how does one find a good one? Usually by asking a doctor or another psychiatrist. But even they have trouble separating the sheep from the goats, because it is so hard to judge from the outside how much help a psychiatrist is actually giving to his patients. If a surgeon's appendix cases all develop post-operative infections, it is clear that the doctor is a bit on the sloppy side. But there is no such criterion in psychiatry. Even a high suicide-rate of patients would not necessarily mean anything against the psychiatrist, since many of his colleagues refuse to accept as patients people with suicidal leanings and therefore have no suicides to be held against them. Also, when some mental patients get well, the credit might go far more to their own will-to-health than to their doctors.

There are not enough psychiatrists to go around, but there is great work being done by the allied professions of clinical psychology and psychiatric social-work. Most mental-hygiene clinics today are set up on the triple basis of a full-time psychiatric social-worker, a full-time psychologist, and a psychiatrist. If a full-time psychiatrist is not available, a part-time psychiatrist or a panel of local psychiatrists who are willing to give some time is substituted.

This team arrangement not only spreads the load and saves the psychiatrist's time but actually offers more help, particularly to children. For, while the psychiatrist or the psychoanalyst is treating the child, the psychiatric social-worker can inquire into the family background and, by working with the parents, try to improve the home situation to which the little patient returns.

In addition to treating some patients, the clinical psychologist administers the diagnostic tests that serve to speed treatment by focusing it earlier than might otherwise be possible on the chief areas of the patient's unconscious conflict. Psychologists also have made and continue to make invaluable contributions in the field of research.

In addition to the help offered by the above-mentioned professionals is the invaluable contribution to the patient's welfare by the psychiatric nurses and hospital aides (formerly called attendants). A hospitalized patient may see his doctor at most for an hour a day, but he sees the nurses or aides over twenty-four hours. And their ability to help him by being patient and understanding with him, no matter what he does, is rarely sufficiently recognized or sufficiently rewarded financially.

Besides these specialists in the psychiatric field, there are people in other fields who, more and more, are being given some psychiatric training. General medical practitioners, public-health nurses, ministers, lawyers, and educators are nowadays better equipped than ever before to pinch-hit for the psychiatrist, and also to recognize when they themselves can no longer be of help and professional treatment by a specialist is necessary.

When a specialist is called in, his first, and frequently exacting, job is to make a diagnosis. Patients almost always complain of both physical and emotional symptoms. Which is the chicken and which the egg? A complete physical examination (given either by the psychiatrist or some other M.D.) and a battery of psychological tests (given either by the psychiatrist or, in most cases, by a clinical psychologist) provide information that the doctor takes into account in trying to decide: (1) what is the matter with the patient; (2) does his problem lie within the doctor's power to treat; (3) can the patient summon enough reserve strength to benefit from treatment; (4) should treatment be deep and long or near the surface and short; or (5) do the patient's symptoms, painful as they are, provide about as good a solution as he could possibly supply for the inner and outer conflicts that beset him?

For although psychiatrists are often able to alleviate inner problems, they are relatively helpless in respect to outer ones. Doctors must always work within the frame of what *is*, not of what might have been. And one of their aims is to help the patient recognize what the realities of his life are and, when these cannot be altered, adjust to them as best he can.

If a patient wants money desperately, the doctor cannot provide him with a get-rich-quick scheme. (If the doctor knew of one, he might be busy at something other than medicine.) But what he can do, if the patient's desire for money seems exorbitant, is to help him gain insight into why he wants it so much. Whom is he trying to outshine,

PARKER © *The Associated Newspapers, Inc.*

and why? Or does money perhaps hold some deep symbolic significance for him which makes him want it more than do other people of similar income? (In some analyses an inordinate desire to hoard money has been found to stem from long-forgotten babyhood attempts to hold back body-wastes in order to frustrate parents, though in other analyses there is no such connection between the two. Furthermore, there are other patients who unconsciously hold back body-wastes for quite different reasons, and there are many people who suffer this identical symptom of constipation because of nothing more complicated than a faulty diet. Hence, careful study by a doctor is needed before any such symbolic act can properly be understood within the context of the patient's life-history; and most parlor dream-analysis and other casual interpretation of irrational behavior is likely to be wide of the mark.)

When Mary came for her first psychiatric interview, she was an ugly girl. The psychiatrist was helpless to change her features. But when he was able to help her feel better, she began to look better. Without knowing quite why, she began to wash and curl her hair, attend to her neglected complexion, hold herself straight, and look the world in the eye. The doctor had enabled an ugly duckling to flower into the attractive young swan that potentially she always had been. "How on earth did you do it?" Mary's mother once asked the social worker who co-operated with the psychiatrist: "She looks like a different girl."

"She's not a different girl," the worker said. "She just feels differently about herself and the world in general."

"But the doctor must have done something," the mother insisted.

"He didn't *do* anything," the worker said. "Mary did it. He helped her to get well but she made most of the effort. If she hadn't, he couldn't have done it for her."

The mother seemed unconvinced—but the worker was telling the truth. Most of what a psychiatrist does is not do anything, but be, despite all provocation to the contrary, both interested and friendly, and remember as much of

RICHTER © *The New Yorker Magazine, Inc.*

what the patient says and how he says it as he possibly can. Then at the strategic moment, like a highly selective re-cording-machine, the psychiatrist may play back some phrase or attitude that the patient is then ready to under-stand in a new way. The psychiatrist is careful to make few judgments and even fewer criticisms. "*Tout comprendre, c'est tout pardonner,*" was coined long before psychiatry—it may not even be wholly true, but such is the feeling that the doctor tries to convey to his patients. He wants them to feel that here, perhaps for the first time in their lives, is someone who is on their side, willing to see things from their point of view, and therefore able to accept everything they can find to tell him.

Occasionally when a patient is simply able to spill out his worries into a sympathetic ear and receive the reassurance that his kind of problem is not unnatural or unspeakable but has been felt and solved by many people, he feels sufficiently better to take the steps necessary to improve his own situation. Or sometimes some new fact or explanation provided by the doctor will enable the patient to see his problem with a new perspective which makes it easier to solve. But in such cases the patient's disturbance was relatively near the surface and his basic adjustment to the deeper problems was already pretty sound.

Such propping up on a temporary jack does not help when the patient's personality needs big structural changes. A new and temporary scaffolding may have to be erected so that the structure does not collapse while the various internal strains and stresses are being shifted about in the interest of soundness and balance. Dr. Carl Binger has written of the "emotional realignment" that occurs in patients during therapy, whereby unconscious energies are shifted from useless or dangerous areas to safe and useful ones. How this happens is not well understood, but in order to clear the way for its happening, the patient must be able to live through again, with the help of the therapist, those repressed feelings and experiences which originally eroded the big basic uprights of his personality.

The temporary scaffolding provided by the psychiatrist is the transference relationship. Because the doctor remains so impersonal, the patient is able to dress him up, as it were, in the garb of either male or female, age or youth, the hostile or the loving, depending on which the key figures of his child-hood happened to be. Naturally, if the patient's repressed

"*My analyst could see right through your analyst!*"

COBEAN © *The New Yorker Magazine, Inc.*

feelings turn out to have been murderous or passionate, the doctor cannot, no matter how permissive he is, allow these to be acted out. But there is no limit to what he can allow to be talked out.

From the doctor's point of view, having the patient trans-fer feelings onto him, even when these are admiring and affectionate,* demands an inordinate degree of self-control.

---

* The old adage "every woman falls in love with her obstetrician" shows how a phenomenon like positive transference was recognized long before Freud gave it a name and taught his students to handle it so as to facilitate therapy.

As one middle-aged woman analyst has described it: "From nine to ten in the morning a smart stockbroker treats me as if I were a financial wizard and I have to keep from indicating the slightest preference between stocks; from ten to eleven a romantic youth treats me as if I were a fairy princess and I have to keep myself from acting at all pleased; from eleven to twelve a woman my age acts as if I were her wise old grandmother and I have to keep from acting at all annoyed. By lunchtime I hardly know who I am any more and the only thing I'm sure of is that all my patients are in some day for an awful letdown."

When the patient's feelings transferred onto the doctor are hostile, an even greater degree of self-control on the doctor's part is necessary. Some emotionally disturbed people exhibit an uncanny ability to search out the tenderest areas in the doctor's own personality and then hammer at these unmercifully. The doctor must summon considerable resources of inner confidence, objectivity, and humor in order to remain calm and friendly and not react in a hurtful or punitive way. For he suspects that the hostile attitude which the patient is currently evidencing stems from a similar one that was once associated with so much pain he cannot bear even now to remember it.

What also helps keep the doctor going is the hope that if he acts in the reverse of the way someone in the patient's past did, the patient may now be able to live through what is called "the corrective emotional experience." This is like one of those movies which, after its tragic ending, flashes back to a fork in the plot and shows how it all could have come out differently and better. The patient quite uncon-

sciously goes back into the feelings that once led to his being hurt or punished and now finds them leading not to
hurt or punishment but to a cheerful acceptance on the

"Why, you swine!"

RICHTER © *The New Yorker Magazine, Inc.*

doctor's part. Somehow this experience brings with it a
strange relief and upsurge of energy. It is as if an old, constantly repeated, jarring chord had resolved itself into a
new and pleasing inner harmony, which in turn releases the
energy that once was wasted in figuratively holding the
hands over the ears.

For example, Jim, who was brought up by a rigid, unloving father and a clinging, finicky mother, reported to
the doctor that as long as he could remember he had suffered tenseness and anxiety whenever he borrowed or owed
something or was given instructions to carry out. Even after

he had fulfilled his duty, he felt that he hadn't done all that was expected of him and kept on worrying. (It was no coincidence, the doctor thought, that the only time Jim had been symptom-free was when he was in the Service, away from home, and doing paperwork that he was capable of doing letter-perfect, and that could be checked immediately by his superior officer.)

Then suddenly, after six months of psychiatric treatment, Jim, who had always meticulously paid his doctor's bill the day after it arrived, stopped paying at all. The doctor, being human, was first tempted to call him on it. But then he wondered whether perhaps Jim's action wasn't wholly unconscious. If so, Jim might be as deeply shamed and guilt-ridden by the doctor's reminder as he used to be when punished by his father or mother for not having done what he was supposed to do.

Furthermore, the doctor realized that part of Jim's problem was that his father, a person who, without meaning to, had undermined Jim's inner security by his unloving attitude, had now asked for a loan that would undermine Jim's financial security. Although the doctor's asking for money would not be for a loan, this further encroachment on Jim's resources might be felt by Jim (whose feelings toward father and doctor were by now pretty well mixed up together) as a further threat.

So the doctor decided to wait and see, and do nothing. He too, like Jim, happened to need money, but he determined to borrow from the bank rather than upset Jim. Several months later Jim came in with a wad of greenbacks

[205

and tossed them onto the doctor's desk. He said he felt very sorry about having forgotten all about paying the doctor, but he didn't look a bit sorry. Rather, he seemed quite ebullient—and he and the doctor were able to discuss what had probably been going on inside Jim all this time. Jim began to realize that by not paying the doctor he had been symbolically rebelling against his father. But the doctor had acted differently from the way Jim's father used to act. Rather than causing Jim to feel unloved and unworthy, the doctor had retained his friendly interest. He simply had waited for Jim to stop acting like a frightened little child— and somehow Jim had stopped feeling like a frightened little child. Jim went through this experience and came out the other side, so to speak, feeling like a responsible man, confident of his own ability to do the right thing, and no longer in need of punishment either by his father or himself (headaches, tenseness, anxiety) in order to get it done.

The doctor could have talked until the cows came home without having as much impact on Jim as did that corrective emotional experience.* Psychiatrists know that there is little point in telling a patient what to do; what they are needed for is to help him become capable of doing what he already knows is worth while. Patients usually arrive for their first interview glutted with good advice from well-meaning friends and relatives. The only trouble with this

---

* There is no telling how many corrective emotional experiences all of us have benefited from without realizing it. Like the Molière character who was amazed to find that what he had been talking all his life was "prose," we may be surprised on looking back over our lives to see that corrective emotional experiences may have been provided by our husband or wife or child or friend when he or she acted in ways that were different from the damaging action of some person further back in our lives.

advice is that the patient is incapable of taking it. He'd love to relax, or snap out of it, or get a grip on himself, or stop being rude to people, or be nicer to his family, or not let himself be upset over little things. But because what stands in his way is a repressed conflict over which he has no conscious control, he needs the help of another person before he can help himself.

The help that the psychiatrist offers doesn't look like much at the beginning. The patient arrives and is asked to sit down or lie back, whichever he prefers, and just talk. The doctor listens carefully to everything that is said—and not said—aware that in time, from out of the apparent chaos, some meaningful pattern will emerge. The patient may describe what is troubling him or he may simply report a recent dream or conversation and discuss what he associates with it at this time, but he brings no notes. The doctor wants to watch the spontaneous trains of thought develop, since, as in a real train, there is bound to be some linkage between the units even if this is not immediately apparent.

The bulk of revelations by patients are concerned with the minutiæ of current daily life, or of past daily life, items of no conceivable interest to anyone but the patient and, because they are of interest to him, also to the doctor. Someone eavesdropping on a psychiatric interview would be as disillusioned as was the little boy who hid behind a park bench at night to find out what lovers talk about. "But it's so boring," he complained. "All they say is things like what they ate for breakfast."

When the patient's talk peters out, the doctor's attitude,

if not what he says, is: "What is it that you don't want to talk about?" For, when a patient can't think of a thing to say (when he "blocks"), or starts looking around the room

"Please, Senator, no prepared statements!"

GOLDSTEIN © *Medical Economics*

discussing inconsequentials, it is a signal to the doctor that some repressed urge or experience has come close to revealing itself. Sometimes the patient will spend the whole hour saying nothing. But this is not necessarily unhelpful, because the doctor's sympathetic readiness to let the patient say, or not say, exactly what he wants to may be so much the opposite of the old parental nagging that, after such a session, the patient may feel free to bring up a great deal of material that might otherwise have taken far longer to come to the surface.

The unconscious force that keeps repressed urges and experiences from reappearing is called resistance. The way it acts might be compared to the reluctance of an underworld

"I wish I could recall the youthful tragedy that marked me so!"

NOFZIGER © PM

character to talk to the cops about anything at all lest unintentionally he incriminate himself. If anyone were watched day and night by a policeman he might start acting furtively and feeling guilty even though he was perfectly innocent. Similarly, the unconscious policeman, by hounding some childish urge or experience that may have been primitive but certainly not wicked to begin with, makes it

start acting as if it were criminal and ought, through resistance, to cover up all its tracks.

This resistance, like the other unconscious defenses,
starts out trying to make our lives easier and happier—and
in many cases succeeds. (Why, after all, should we constantly be subject to being reminded of what we are anxious
to forget, if not to forgive?) But because, like them, it is
impervious to time and to reason, it often interferes with
a patient's sincere desire to give the doctor a full and true
picture. Whenever any of the patient's unconscious defenses go into high gear, the doctor has a pretty good idea
that it is resistance that is spurring them on. At such times
the patient either:

> forgets his appointment;
> or absolutely denies the existence of some common human
> failing in himself;
> or admits this failing but rationalizes its existence through
> a complicated network of excuses (methinks the lady protests
> too much);
> or projects his undesirable feelings onto other people (per-
> haps accusing the doctor of hating him);
> or displaces them onto other objects (perhaps telling the
> doctor he hates coming there because of the doctor's "smelly
> pipe" or "ugly office");
> or isolates his feelings (perhaps reporting some tragic per-
> sonal experience with evident numbness or boredom);
> or allows magic thinking to enter the picture (a feminine
> patient, perhaps, during the positive phase of the transfer-
> ence trying to act as if she and the doctor had been stranded
> on a desert island);
> or shows signs of reaction-formation (perhaps suddenly re-

fusing to recline on the doctor's couch, and instead sitting bolt upright with a lethal-looking umbrella kept near at hand);

or *regresses* to the point where he feels he must phone the doctor at all hours to verify the tiniest decision;

or *daydreams* to an exorbitant degree.

And a sign of improvement which delights both patient and doctor is the lessening of resistance. The patient begins to talk more freely, and the above-mentioned unconscious defenses are gradually replaced by suppression, sublimation, or laughter.

Even before resistance diminishes there is an unconscious force at work in the patient which allies itself with the doctor in his attempt to find out what's bothering the patient. This is the human urge to let the truth be known. "Murder will out." What the patient really means may, through a slip of the tongue, sneak out past what he intended to say. Or some unconscious action, like forgetting to pick up his mother-in-law, may indicate what his true feelings are. Sometimes in dreams, too, the disguises become so transparent that the inner meaning shines clearly through.

When the psychiatrist interprets slips of the tongue or dreams or, as more often happens, reinforces the patient's own interpretation of them, the patient may get a feeling like that of Archimedes when the theory of displacement of water popped into his head and he ran from his bathtub right into the street, shouting: "Eureka! (I have found it!)" A light really does dawn sometimes, and this is a sign that the treatment has struck pay dirt at last.

Another sign of improvement in the patient which pleases the doctor but may be agonizing to the patient is the temporary replacement of the original symptoms by

"*Gentlemen: Regarding your garter of the fourteenth . . .*"

DAY © *The New Yorker Magazine, Inc.*

the anxiety that unconsciously has been underlying them. Freud called this overwhelming uneasiness "free-floating anxiety," and it may cause nightmares, temper outbursts, depression, fatigue, or inability to concentrate. The one demand the psychiatrist makes before starting therapy is that the patient make no big decision, no marriage, no divorce, or shift of job, without thorough discussion with the doctor. For patients may temporarily feel so desperate that they are likely to do something rash in order to escape the black cloud that is with them day and night and against which they are helpless to fight.

Many feel as one patient did when his headaches disappeared in favor of this anxiety and he begged to be allowed to have them back. Patients also say that, unpleasant as the treatment hour may be, the times in between are even worse, when the reassuring presence of the doctor is lacking and the old hobgoblins of the past refuse to quiet down. Yet such emotional "working through" is usually necessary before any lasting relief is possible.

At the end of treatment most psychiatric patients report having felt worse before feeling better. This is, in a way, no more surprising than that the surgical lancing of an abscess should hurt more than leaving it alone. But once the festering material is out, the easing of pressure may be blissful. Nor does the psychiatrist, any more than the surgeon, stop there. Both want to see to it that, after the patient is rid of what was poisoning him, healing can take place in as therapeutic a surrounding as possible. Both doctors may insist on hospitalization or, in any event, on avoidance of strain. The patient is not supposed to work too hard or subject himself too frequently to the people or situations that originally caused his distress.

Families of psychiatric patients sometimes find this difficult to understand. They love the patient more than the doctor does. So how can it be that the doctor can help the patient more than they can? What is hard to explain to them is that the doctor can help the patient precisely because he is objective and not emotionally involved with him. Psychiatrists are disqualified from professionally treating people to whom they are personally attached, just as surgeons are forbidden to operate on their own children or obstetricians to deliver their own wives. Scientific detachment is one of the doctor's chief tools.

Of course the psychiatrist cannot be one hundred per cent detached. His humanness is ineradicable. But he is trained to limit it and also to harness it through what Freud called the counter-transference. This is the process by which the doctor studies his own feelings to see what they can tell him about the patient's. For example, if the doctor begins to feel affectionate toward the patient, he stops to wonder whether the patient might not be harboring a similar feeling that, on a tit-for-tat basis, is evoking that of the doctor. Further search may turn up evidence of this perhaps totally unconscious feeling on the patient's part—or it may only show that the doctor, because of his own emotional past, is so much in need of affection for himself that he wishfully reads it into other people. Here the doctor's training analysis is of inestimable value, enabling him to look into himself with more knowledge and objectivity than would otherwise be possible.

Or the doctor may find that although the patient is quite prompt, polite, and co-operative, the doctor is constantly being irritated by him. Why? Here again the doctor must question whether the patient is harboring aggressive feelings that are likely to arouse similar feelings in the doctor, or whether the patient simply reminds the doctor of someone unpleasant in his own past. Thus the doctor must play a double role: one as a human bit of litmus paper that unconsciously registers the emotions of the patient, and one as the specialist trained in deciphering this litmus paper's wide range of colors.

A frequent sign of masked hostility in patients is the complaint that the doctor is charging too much or cutting the treatment hour short or in some way cheating the patient. This is not to say that psychiatry is the sole profession to contain no chiselers; some few psychiatrists have indeed overcharged their patients. But the majority of their fellows ask fees that are not, when measured by the years of necessary training, out of line with the fees of other specialists. Of course, because the patient comes more often to the psychiatrist than, say, to the oculist, he feels the drain on his pocketbook more sharply. But this is like one of the Two Black Crows who found out that his white horses ate more than his black horses because "dere was more of de white horses."

Therefore, in general, the patients' accusations in the sphere of fees, being objectively unfounded, are probably emotionally based; and actually psychiatrists do not too much mind this signal of hostility because they have found that patients tend to make more of an effort during the treatment hour if they feel they have to pay well for it. This effort by patients to get their money's worth may save them both time and money in the end, and free the doctor to help more people. Psychiatrists can carry only a small patient load because treatment is so time-consuming, and many have substantial waiting-lists. Yet the longer a patient has to wait, the longer his treatment may eventually take, since in psychiatry as well as in the other branches of medicine the earlier treatment can start the shorter its duration is likely to be.

LANGDON © *Bradbury, Agnew & Co., Ltd.*

Most practicing psychiatrists carry some patients at reduced rates or without charge, but their efforts fall far short of filling the need. The people of the lower-income groups in twentieth-century America have little more psychiatric assistance available, outside of the overcrowded public mental-hospitals, than if they were living in the Middle Ages. The little that they have comes by way of the Veterans Administration hospitals, the U.S. Public Health Service, and the sparsely situated community clinics.

But why should anyone go through such a long-drawn-out process as psychotherapy when there are short-cuts available like hypnosis and drugs? Because, although these may often speed a cure, they do not make it stick. Something more lasting than hypnosis or drugs alone is needed, as Freud discovered when the symptoms of his hypnotized patients eventually returned.

Hypnosis is the production of a sleeplike state in the patient by the doctor. No one knows what it consists of, but while it lasts the patient acts as if the hypnotist and his own self were one and the same. There are definite limits beyond which hypnosis will have no effect. If the patient does not know how to talk French, being ordered to do so will have no result. Nor can patients be induced to perform acts that go completely against the grain. Another limitation is that only about one in twenty persons is susceptible to hypnosis. Some few psychoanalysts, however, today find good results through hypnoanalysis, which is a combination of hypnosis and psychoanalysis.

Narcoanalysis, the combination of drugs whose effect is not unlike that of alcohol with psychoanalysis, is also used to good avail in special cases. These drugs cause a "twilight sleep," rather like the state we all experience just before dropping off at night. Under their influence the patient may be able to remember in detail events he has little or no memory of when conscious. Like the other forms of medicine, psychiatry can sometimes use drugs to good advantage. During the last war, for example, sodium pentathol and sodium amytal (the so-called truth serums) were used in helping soldiers remember the events that had triggered their emotional distress. It always takes some final straw to break the camel's back, and in these war cases the "straw" was often more like a ton of bricks that crushed the patient so hard and so fast that consciously he never knew what hit him.

Why certain people survive harrowing experiences relatively intact, why other people get sick from them and then are able to be cured, and why still other people get sick from them and so far cannot be cured, is not yet well understood. Factors called resilience, stamina, frustration-tolerance, and ego-strength have a lot to do with it, but just what these consist of and how they can be more fully developed is still very much in the research stage.

Today preventive psychiatry means early treatment and, most of all, research that may furnish the knowledge needed to prevent mental disorder. Early detection and early treatment can be practiced in community clinics, private offices, in the clinics of schools and colleges, and in the dispensaries of the armed forces. The best preventive psychiatry will probably be practiced in marriage-counseling centers and in well-baby clinics.

For the people who need help (estimated as one in fifteen) there is, besides individual therapy, the new and hopeful group therapy. Here people with the same kind of problem, such as marital difficulties or alcoholism, often find support and understanding through frequent discussion-meetings, sometimes with a trained leader and sometimes without. Here there can be analysis of one member by another, transference onto one member by another, and revealing by all in turn of long-secret experiences without fear of condemnation or ridicule.

Sometimes all verbal therapeutic methods fail, and then the more extreme measures of electric convulsive therapy and insulin shock treatment may be used. Some psychotic patients respond well to shock, most spectacularly those whose illness is found to be connected with the change of life. With other patients, particularly schizophrenics, shock treatment may serve to make them accessible, sometimes for the first time in years, to verbal therapy. For a few minutes after the treatment, or a few hours, or a few days, these deluded or withdrawn patients may come to life long enough to listen to the doctor and, even more important, to talk meaningfully about their own basic urges and experiences. How shock treatment works, scientists do not yet know. But, judiciously handled, this form of treatment has returned to normal life many patients who might otherwise have remained in institutions, including some who had already been "put away" for life.

Mental hospitals are relatively new. One hundred and fifty years ago the insane were locked up in jails. Today doctors feel that many of our mental hospitals are still too reminiscent of jails, with inmates locked far away from homes and loved ones. Recently, as a result of the activities of Clifford Beers's mental-hygiene group, now the National Association for Mental Health, there has been much improvement. Attempts are being made to have mental patients treated in special wings of local general hospitals rather than in distant and specialized institutions. When patients are treated closer to their community, they can be put on an outpatient basis earlier than at present, thus freeing needed beds for others. Eventually the bulk of our permanent patients in institutions will be made up only of those who might constitute a real danger to other people or themselves, and those senile and feebleminded patients who are beyond recall.

At the moment, half the hospital beds in the United States are filled with mental cases, of which half will stay for the rest of their lives. If treatment had been active and early and nearer home, it is safe to say that many of these patients could be leading constructive lives on the outside, although some of them still would be coming to the hospital for occasional treatment. From the taxpayer's point of view, a great deal of money now spent for research and treatment of mental illness will save a great deal more money and incalculable human suffering in the future.

The mental patient's own suffering does not always continue. Repression, resistance, and the other unconscious defenses occasionally succeed in their attempt to keep the conscious self from feeling pain. And in the hospital setting, where outward demands are not made on the patients, some of the very sick ones do not appear to suffer at all.

They reach a stage of stupor. But their families are still suffering. That old-fashioned stigma attached to mental illness has not yet been overcome, despite the fact that it is often the sensitive, brilliant, vibrant people who succumb to mental illness, rather than the clodlike and dull. Some day people may progress to the point of regarding the having out of their unconscious conflicts no more of a disgrace than the having out of their tonsils. But there will still remain to the family the sorrow of seeing a loved one who is "not himself."

Today, as a last resort, families of severe, chronic neurotics and psychotics agree to neurosurgery as a form of relief of symptoms. The brain operations of lobotomy and topectomy sever nerve connections in the brain and cause a reduction of anxiety. But they sometimes, though by no means always, leave the patient with less verve than he used to have. He can often return home, take care of his family, keep his job, and certainly have a far better life than he would have in a mental hospital to the end of his days. But psychosurgery should be resorted to only after thorough examination of the patient by a psychiatrist who knows both organic and psychotherapeutic medicine. What the doctor has to decide is whether the patient's suffering is so terrible that a real chance should be taken of limiting, not so much his I.Q., which often shows no reduction, but his uniquely human subtlety of feeling and thinking.

Will Power* and Knowledge

◇◇

The happy man lives subconsciously today among thoughts that he will render articulate tomorrow. Nothing is more exciting (you can see hints and murmurs of it in all sorts of places) than to watch the world getting ready to think ideas quite different from those it is at the moment openly proclaiming.

CHRISTOPHER MORLEY

ONE THEORY of why God created man as such a foolish creature is that God, by definition perfect, could never know the joy of improvement, and man, who has so much room for it, very often can.

Why is it such fun to learn, to gain new skills and controls? Why are we filled with sublime discontent and unwillingness to remain mere lumps? It is true that we are rewarded as children by our parents when we improve—but

* The term "will power" is used here in its ordinary, everyday sense. Will power has never been defined to the full satisfaction of the philosophers, theologians, and psychiatrists who have tried their hands at it—and probably never will be. But all of us know what it feels like to make up our minds to do something and then do it. This experience, although largely conscious, is none the less also subject to the laws of the unconscious (described in Chapter i).

why do *they* care? Someone must have once got a kick out of having things done right for a change, and started the original rewarding process. But who? This chapter will raise more questions than it can answer, and will offer more conjectures than facts, since the writers are returning to the area of daily normal living, where the reader may know as much or more than they, and where none of us, as is evident in the sad state of our world, knows enough.

Normal daily life is walking a tightrope between satisfying our basic urges and feelings on the one hand and following the rules of our society on the other. Small wonder that all of us at times halt, stagger, or even temporarily lose our balance.

Psychiatrists are sometimes thought of as revolutionary because they weigh the effects of society's taboos. But, since their job is to help patients live happily in that society in which they find themselves, with all its taboos that can't be changed overnight, psychiatrists often end up wielding a conservative influence. They know only too well that although the abnormal person can swim out far and long from the shore of society's approval, the normal person must eventually return or drown. Normal people cannot stand being too different. And, ironically, it is often after having conformed to the rules of the game, thereby winning the respect of other people, that an individual can effect such changes in those rules as he believes necessary. Nothing being static in this world, we can each set going a tiny chain reaction of influence which affects the attitudes and behavior of other people just as our attitudes and behavior are sometimes affected by them.

It's all true.

© Abner Dean

One of the least static societies in the world's history is our current American one. Most of us, with the exception

"They were quite wealthy at one time."

HENDERSON © *Saturday Evening Post*

of a great many nonwhite citizens, are not locked by birth into one place, one kind of job, one position in society. We hope to go up, although sometimes we go down, or sideways. Over a hundred years ago a visitor from Vienna was amazed at how in America "doctors sometimes become building contractors, colonels are innkeepers, and pianists, grocers." Today people move around even more, geographically and economically, and win approval for improving their situations. A Horatio Alger who rises "from rags to

[225

riches" is in a way more admired than the person "to the manor born," who ostensibly has no place further to go.

But when the sky's the limit, how can we ever be satisfied with our lot, which is only a little way up? Man's imagination allows him to picture a being far nearer perfection than he in reality can ever be. Furthermore, we all apparently start out with infantile ideas of omnipotence—and even in adolescence our private dreams are to set the world on fire as it has never been set before. American boys are told, and sometimes secretly believe, that they will become President. American girls are told, and sometimes secretly believe, that they will either become President or, like Cinderella, be swooped up by a Prince Charming riding a white Cadillac and taken to live happily ever after on Country Club Hill. Uniquely privileged as we are, to be living in a country where there are so few outer obstacles to individual success, must we not sometimes mobilize all our inner resources in order to avoid feeling paralyzed by inferiority because, having been taught and wanting very much to believe that dreams come true, we grow up to find that our particular one has not?

In attempting this kind of adjustment to reality, the bringing of our unconscious desires and fears to consciousness may help. For then we can take an objective look and, like the oyster, try to coat or digest those desires and fears which in adult life are no longer of any use to us. When we make a mature, conscious appraisal of our own inborn talents, which in combination with one another are unlike anyone else's, we may be able to gain great satisfaction from focusing them well on some few areas (" 'tis a poor thing but mine own"). Why should we, after all, like children, unconsciously demand the impossible for ourselves, or expect the impossible of ourselves, or take full blame onto ourselves when the impossible does not come to pass?

Together with such an inward accounting, it sometimes helps us to make an outward one, too, by stacking up our personal strengths and weaknesses against the premiums put upon these by the time in which we live. Had Columbus been born today, with no physical continents left to discover, he might have ended up with an inferiority complex and no mention in the history books. Similarly, any of us might have found greater opportunities to make use of our own talents had we been born into some other period or class in society. Still the problem remains, we are as we are and what can we do about it?

Here we run up against another of the many contradictions in our culture. We are taught: "A man's reach should exceed his grasp," and also: "For what we have received, let us be grateful." Both are true enough, but how to reconcile them? If it hadn't been the unconscious insatiability and the conscious ambition of the human animal, we'd probably still be shrieking to one another from the treetops; yet if there were not some relaxation and satisfaction to be gained from goals partially achieved, even small goals, we would hardly have the impetus to keep going. Here is another tightrope to waver our way across. And it is important that we try, not only for the sake of our own peace of mind but also for the sake of the people with whom we live and work. For extremely discontented, tightly strung, and anxious individuals do not make the best husbands or wives, bosses or employees, friends or neighbors, or, from the point of view of the future perhaps most important of all, the best parents.

For it is rare, if it ever happens, that a child is able to

HUDSON © *Fawcett Publications, Inc.*

fulfill all the unconscious ambitions of both mother and father. A baby girl might have been a boy, or vice versa; an athletic child an intellectual one, or vice versa; a stupid, or even a bright, child brighter. Without meaning to, parents are likely to load children with the burden of their own unconscious yearnings, and therefore many children grow up with deep inferiority feelings because they *can't* satisfy their parents no matter what they do.

On a conscious level, of course, we realize that such parental attitudes aren't fair, that a child can't help the way it was born. But it often takes considerable investigation of why we feel ourselves to be disappointing to our parents or, in turn, why we feel unduly irritated by our own child, in order to rise above such attitudes.

"I haven't just got an inferiority complex—I am inferior."

BAILEY © *Saturday Evening Post*

For example, we are consciously aware that all children must at some time rebel against parental edicts in order to try out their own wings and gain strength for the time when the parents are no longer around. But sometimes this disobedience on our part toward our parents is accompanied by our feeling disproportionate guilt and anxiety. And sometimes this disobedience on the part of our own child toward us is accompanied by our feeling disproportionate

[229

hostility and rage. Then is the time to ask ourselves why is it so important to our parents, on the one hand, or to ourselves, on the other, that a child be docile? Were they, or we, forced into a pattern of docility as children which is unconsciously (through identification) being carried on? Or is it that they, or we, were given too much license as children and are unconsciously (through reaction-formation) rebelling against that? Are they, or we, so full of unconscious inferiority feelings that a child's challenging is felt as a threat? Or does the desire for a model child reflect a similar inferiority-based need to impress the neighbors? In other words, how much of any parental haranguing is really at the self and how much at the child?

This is hard work, attempting to make the unconscious conscious. It is hard when we are trying to understand our parents and other people, and even harder when we are trying to understand ourselves. Perhaps the reason Shakespeare put the famous advice, "to thine own self be true," into the mouth of that old fool, Polonius, was that he knew it could never fully be accomplished. As with the onion, we peel back a layer of our personality only to come promptly upon another layer. Sometimes the only thing to do is to recognize the existence of a particular problem, consciously formulate it as clearly as we can, and then wait for time and the parts of ourselves which are not too deeply unconscious to work together in finding an answer.

Like the farmer who can tell which wild animals have recently been causing trouble for him by the tracks, the toothmarks, and the droppings, we can learn to spot which of our unconscious defenses have recently been causing trouble for us. But like an unlucky farmer, we can never quite catch sight of them in action: they move too fast for us. Thus time, even if it is only a few seconds, is needed between the action of an unconscious defense and the spotting of it; and even more time is needed for us to judge whether this was an isolated appearance or part of a significant procession. Then if we know, say, that a whole pack of rationalizations has, of late, been invading our behavior, we can either try to set up fences of conscious determination against their reappearance, or try to avoid the kind of situation which has tempted them into action, or, if these methods do not work, breathe a deep sigh and try to see what kind of unconscious conflict underlies their sudden, unusual activity.

On the other hand, there is no earthly reason to inquire why we behave as we do most of the time. If a farm is functioning adequately, why stay up all night and poke around? Every now and then it's good to check to see that all is going well. And to do this some knowledge is necessary. But if we stop and check up all the time we'll never get any work done. Unless something is clearly out of order, we are better off just attending to our daily round and enjoying it as much as we can.

When there is evidence of trouble in ourselves and on investigation we find that the villain has been our unconscious policeman, we may, as we release some of our actions from his control, run a risk of their getting temporarily out of hand. There is no danger of overeating when our stomach is upset—but when this condition is cleared up we may be tempted to gorge ourselves. Similarly, a young woman suffering from frigidity might never feel disposed toward making love. But once she gains insight into the causes of this frigidity and works through the repressed emotions involved, she might feel very much tempted and have to substitute for the old unconscious billy such conscious willpower and knowledge as she had, up to then, been able to develop.

Will power and knowledge, like muscles, grow through use. Practice, of course, does not make perfect, but it certainly helps. At the beginning of the training season a sudden heavy strain or overexertion should be avoided. Gentle loads gradually increased are probably best, since will power developed in small things will be available for big ones. Just what will power is, to what extent conscious and unconscious, philosophers have always wondered and psychiatry continues to explore. All we know to date is that although unconscious urges powerfully affect, and sometimes even determine, what our goals are and whether we reach them or not, conscious volition can always step in either on the side of these unconscious forces or against them. Besides our being puppets liable to be pulled by invisible strings, we also are capable of exerting considerable pressure on the puppeteer.

If we want not to eat too much, we can consciously keep ourselves out of the kitchen and thereby physically prevent ourselves from being confronted by irresistible temptation. Our unconscious, that sly dog, may then try to persuade us, say, that the only pencil we can write with is the one hanging over the stove, but with insight we can keep from being lured into that delicious-smelling kitchen. We have to get

up early in the morning, so to speak, to keep one jump
ahead of our own unconscious, but if we want to enough,
and try often enough, we can do it.

Different people exert will power in different ways at different times. For some occasions *suppression* works best: a

*"Gerald has a will of iron—but he seldom gets a chance to
use it."*

GOLDSTEIN © *Saturday Evening Post*

dieter may simply not allow himself to think about food; he
will throw himself into his work or go for long walks or in
some other way distract himself. For other occasions *controlled fantasy* works best: a dieter may synthetically as-
suage his hunger pangs by devouring with his eyes the
luscious food-advertisements that abound in our magazines.

For still other occasions *insight* works best: once the dieter understands that his undue craving for food is based on emotional causes, food may lose some of its appeal for him. Whichever method is used will, if we are lucky, be reinforced by the unconscious defenses of humor or sublimation. In some way that is not understood, what we call strength of character in ourselves (and tend to call stubbornness in our children) involves unconscious reinforcement of consciously made choices.

Not only is the process of exerting will power different from that of repression, but the results may be different too. For example, after the valiant dieter has denied himself food until he reaches normal weight, his will power and conscious knowledge allow him to enjoy eating normally again. But if it had been some repressed conflict about food that was causing him not to eat, he might well continue not eating long after becoming underweight. Being completely unconscious of what was causing his unhappiness at the dinner table, he could perhaps make use of his will power to force himself to eat, but he could not, all by himself, correct the underlying attitude of revulsion which was preventing his body from benefiting from the nourishment taken in.

On the other hand, repression as well as all our unconscious tendencies have, within limits, an important and valuable place in our lives.* We never can—and wouldn't even want to—fully escape their operations:

---

* The value of the unconscious *defenses*, with their varying degrees of repression, was included in the separate description of each in Chapter iii.

Without some unconscious symbolic thinking, we might never be able to search for the truth or communicate with other people by way of words or numbers.

Without some unconscious inconsistency and imperviousness to time and reason, we might never be able to laugh.

Without some unconscious momentum, we might never be able to devote our lives unswervingly to any ideal.

Without some unconscious seeking of pleasure and avoiding of pain, we might never have any fun.

And without tit-for-tat, we might not survive, since instinctive reactions work faster than conscious thought and often split-second timing saves lives. If someone sneaks up behind us in a dark alley and hits us on the head, we do just as well to hit him back first and ask questions later.

Similarly, society would have a hard time surviving were it not for our tendency, when someone does something nice for us, to do something nice for him—or for someone else. But in the area of tit-for-tat perhaps more than in any other, will power and knowledge are needed in order to control and redirect this tendency so that it does good rather than harm.

If someone is cranky and disagreeable, and we automatically become disagreeable right back at him, we are neither helping him nor are we likely to achieve what we had hoped for in relation to him, whether this be something intangible, like friendliness, or tangible, like a meal being properly served. But if we apply will power to conquering our first annoyance, and knowledge to figuring out what is bothering him, we may end up both helping him and also getting what we want. This applies to our attitude toward people of every age and station, but is perhaps most dramatic in our attitude toward children.

[235

FRADON © *The New Yorker Magazine, Inc.*

For example, the behavior of the next-older child when a new baby arrives may be quite hateful. If at such times the child's hostility, which is caused by terror that he has lost his parents' love, is met on a tit-for-tat basis by the parents'

236]

becoming hostile in return, the child's fear of being un-loved will seem justified. The very feelings of deep inferi-ority and anxiety which, to begin with, caused his bad be-havior will be exacerbated rather than relieved. A vicious cycle of hostility (the child's) leading to hostility (the par-ents') to further hostility (on the part of both) may be set up. But if, instead, when the jealous child behaves badly, warm arms come around him and he is asked please won't he be a big helper during these months when mother and father are busy with the tiresome little newcomer (who is too young, fortunately, to understand what is being said about him), the older child's hostility may drain away and be replaced by a healthy, though from the parental point of view equally irksome, strutting self-importance.

Thus parents have it in their power to allow a deadlock of hostile emotions to develop until child and parent are so at war that they can't imagine how to start making peace, and outside help may be needed. Or parents, by will power and knowledge, can prevent this deadlock from originating by curbing the initial tit-for-tat reaction in themselves and then substituting open eyes and ears for blind emotion. In-deed they can often start a benign tit-for-tat cycle going instead, since loving encouragement on their part may cause the child to want to please them, which in turn would lead to further loving encouragement, to further efforts to please, until child and parent become immensely satisfied with themselves and each other.

This is, of course, far easier said than done. In fact, par-ents, being human, can't possibly use self-control all the time.* But in the long run the harder way for the parent at the beginning may end up easier all around. When a child is hateful to other children, we can't expect other children not to be hateful in return. But if an adult is sometimes able to counter a child's hatefulness with the mature form of meekness which comes from quiet strength, the child may learn by example that there are reactions other than the immediate and automatic kind, and he may even some day, by trying these out for himself, find how effective they can be. Here, in short, is psychiatry's rediscovery, on the basis of studying thousands of cases of ex-hateful children, of the value of that lesson taught by Jesus which, as Judge Learned Hand has said, "mankind has never learned and never forgotten."

In the earliest books of the Old Testament the tit-for-tat or talion principle was held to be the basis of just action: "Eye for eye,** tooth for tooth, hand for hand, foot for foot." Yet in one of these same books (Leviticus), there appeared the challenging command: "Love thy neighbor as thyself." This did not mean to love him only when he was good or pleasant or friendly, but all the time, just as all the time we love, in the sense of look out for, ourselves. Gradually this concept developed into the belief that God also loved man not only when he was good or pleasant or friendly, but all the time and despite his sins. The idea of the just God slowly gave way to the idea of the merciful God.

---

* As one harassed modern mother cried: "At least one valuable lesson I'm teaching my child: that human beings are inconsistent."

** Actually this was a mild edict compared to the practice of many of the neighboring tribes, which was to administer death as punishment for the destruction of an eye.

In the later parts of the Bible, the emphasis shifted over further from vengeance and punishment to forgiveness and love. We find ourselves admonished to love not only our neighbor but even our enemy. Why? Why should we try

COBEAN © *The New Yorker Magazine, Inc.*

to forgive those who have trespassed against us? Why should we force ourselves—and forcing it often is—to "return good for evil?" Because, for one thing, as Paul quotes the Proverbs in explaining, it works; it pays off:

> If thine enemy hunger, feed him; if he thirst, give him drink: for in so doing thou shalt heap coals of fire on his head.

This is no sweetness-and-light admonishment. This is power politics as practiced between individuals. The fact of the matter is that normally we have no defense against defenselessness. What can we do if the child we are scolding suddenly runs and hides its face in our lap? Or when some

[239

fool driver who tangles bumpers with us sheepishly apolo-
gizes? We are undone; our fangs are drawn. Nor is the dis-
arming quality of helpessness felt only by human beings.
Dogs and wolves, as observed by the Austrian biologist,
Konrad Lorenz, unless they were starving or what he called
"psychopathic," stopped fighting as soon as their opponent
lay down on its back with its chin up and turned to the
right, exposing the jugular vein, as if to say, "kill me if you
must, but I won't fight back." (People with pets may have
witnessed this same phenomenon of the puppy groveling
when the big dog growls, yet none the less succeeding in
driving the long-suffering big dog away from his favorite
snoozing-ground.) *Animals too seem to know the power
that can be exerted by turning the other cheek.* But this
action of theirs, being instinctive rather than selective, may
also open the way to serious trouble. Dogs and wolves that
exposed their jugular vein to a starving or to a mentally ill
opponent did not live to tell the tale.

Human beings also run considerable risk when we turn
the other cheek automatically rather than selectively. We
need to use all our conscious and unconscious discernment
to judge when this power should be put to use and when it
might lead to abuse. As the Lorenz observation of animals
indicated, there were two conditions in the opponent which
made turning the other cheek in his direction too hazardous
to be worth trying. One condition was starvation; the other,
mental illness. These same two conditions may well apply
to human beings also. If a person is starving, in the sense
that his basic urges have been so utterly frustrated that he
feels driven, no matter what the cost, to satisfy them; or if

a person is mentally ill, in the sense that his unconscious anxiety has mounted to the point that he feels driven, no matter what the cost, to perform irrational acts, his opponent had better stay on guard. For, either way, the person may not be able to prevent himself from exercising such power as our defenselessness might give him; he may, in effect, no longer have the requisite freedom of choice.

This freedom of choice, or free will, will probably always remain a considerable mystery to the human being who, like the swimmer, operates to such a great extent beneath the surface. As with normality, we may know when we have lost it, but we may not know, at the time, when we have it. And although we usually can tell when it is being outwardly encroached upon, we usually cannot tell when it is being inwardly encroached upon. Sometimes we make what we consider to be a free and unbiased decision in view of the facts and later find that our decision had less to do with the facts than with our own unconscious predilections. Or we may go ahead and act on what we recognize to be only a hunch and later find that this action was more in accord with the facts than our conscious mind could possibly have realized at the time. Sometimes we do what we choose to do; sometimes we do what we have to do; and just where the fine line between them is, nobody has ever been able— or probably ever will be able—to say.

One modern theory is that, from a biological point of view, man's freedom of choice expanded as he evolved into being the only bisexual animal not driven for short periods of time, of which the duration was beyond his control, by a mating instinct so overpowering that its acting out was also beyond his control. As nature stopped controlling man's sexual behavior for him, he became better able to control it for himself. Because he had all year to make love, he no longer felt compelled on any one day to make love to the first member of the opposite sex who happened along. He became free to choose when, where, and to whom to make love, or whether not to make love at all. And as this urge became more compressible in man than in any other animal he also became the only one to divert its huge power into activities not directly connected with it.

It is, after all, only when an urge is not absolutely overwhelming that we can be said to be master of it, rather than it the master of us. There are reports of many a person so starved for food that he could not prevent himself from devouring far more than his shrunken stomach could bear, and, as a result, being forced to lose it all again. For his sake someone else had to limit his freedom of action in relation to food because he was temporarily incapable of limiting it for himself.

Similarly, according to most psychiatric theory, a profound emotional starvation during infancy and childhood in relation to the basic urges may set up such an insatiability that even a gorging in later life may not bring satisfaction. This kind of deep frustration is not the same as repression, although the two often cause similar results. They are different in that while we may be quite aware of what our frustrations are, we cannot, by definition, be aware of what our repressions are. The results of the two are similar in that both can set up such unbearable tension that normal activity does not serve to dispel it, and the person may be forced into some form of abnormal activity. This abnormal activity in turn may set up such hostility, fear, or unconscious tension in other people that the original frustration or repression, rather than being relieved, is augmented.

"I'm so hungry I could eat a horse!"

WYMA © *Collier's*

Thus the person who is driven into abnormality of action by long-frustrated or repressed basic urges is often the very one who might benefit most by the sudden relaxation of tension which comes when an opponent goes limp and doesn't fight back. Yet most of us don't want to take the chance of making ourselves even temporarily helpless in relation to a person who apparently has so little freedom of choice that he cannot bring himself to behave normally.

Is there anyone better equipped than the rest of us to help such a person?

In our society there are two groups of people whose professional training includes practice in how and when to turn the other cheek without undue danger to themselves. These two groups can each help a different kind of troubled person, and sometimes both can help the same person. More and more these two groups are learning to work together.

One group consists of the ministers who, when confronted by the intense suffering of "starving" or mildly disturbed parishioners, do not compound their already existing anxiety and guilt by berating them, but instead appeal to divine understanding and forgiveness for their sake.* Because of the parishioner's faith in God's love, this appeal may serve to break into the vicious and often unconscious cycle of emotions, of fear leading to hate leading to guilt and back to fear again. At first tentatively, and then with increasing confidence, he may try out the more constructive emotions, which in turn may lead to a benign internal cycle and to an improvement of his relations with other people.

The other group consists of psychiatrists, psychoanalysts, psychotherapists, psychologists, and psychiatric social-workers, who can sometimes help not only a "starving" or mildly disturbed person but even a seriously disturbed person (whom the minister cannot help). These professionals call not on divine power, but on the kind of scientific objectivity and patience which have for centuries been practiced

---

* One of the most memorable examples in fiction was The Bishop in Les Misérables who, when ex-galley-slave Valjean was apprehended with The Bishop's silver, pretended he had given it to him.

by other doctors and nurses. As much as is humanly possible, they make themselves into an imperturbable backboard
against which the patient can bat old unconscious hates and
fears and guilts without fear of retaliation. Somehow
through this process the patient begins to develop insight
and control which he never had before. And he too, at first
perhaps with the doctor's encouragement and support, and
later by himself, may try out more creative emotions.

Moreover, although the rest of us, without professional
training, cannot apply these principles in a curative way to
relative strangers or to "starving" or disturbed people, we
can often apply them in a preventive way to a person we
love when he or she is dejected or cantankerous. The very
existence of our mutual love lends to us an insulation and
also a power in regard to him that other people (nonpro-
fessionals) do not have in regard to him and that we do not
have in regard to other people (whom we do not love). We
can take a lot more nonsense from him (without even being
tempted to hit back) and we can also do a lot more for him
(because what we say really matters to him). When he
comes to us for help—often without being aware that this
is what he is doing—we do not say to him, as a casual ac-
quaintance might, or as we might say to a casual acquaint-
ance: "If you will do thus and so, then I'll be on your side."
What we say, in effect, is, "I'm on your side, old dear, no
matter what."

The support which this kind of unconditional affection
gives is immensely precious. All of us, probably because of
the unconscious conflicts and anxiety left over from our
childhood, seem to slip sometimes into a quicksand of de-

pression or disagreeableness from which, by ourselves, we cannot even get a leg up. If, at such times, another person presses on us even a little by adverse criticism or some form of (tit-for-tat) disagreeableness, we may sink to such a depth that not only our happiness but our effectiveness is impaired. But if another person provides us with a sturdy platform of affection, we may be able to heave ourselves up and out.

This platform can be supplied by way of another person's understanding (all loads are lightened when shared), or by way of another person's acceptance (if he knows the worst about us and still can love us, then perhaps we're worth retrieving after all), or by way of another person's faith.

Faith, according to its famous definition, is "the substance of things hoped for, the evidence of things not seen." Sometimes it is so strong that people gladly give their lives for it. Sometimes it is so wobbly that the first puff of wind blows it over. Aside from faith in God, which is a subject far beyond the scope of this book, there are two things which one person can help another person to have faith in: one is in himself, the second is in other people. (In sick people the faith in self may reach disproportionate delusions of power on the one hand and utter self-abnegation on the other; and faith in other people can similarly range the two abnormal extremes.)

Gradually we are learning that when a person has been encouraged to do his best and is given jobs he can do well, his faith in himself is increased; while, if he has been discouraged and is given jobs that are beyond his power to do well, his faith in himself is diminished.* It is quite true that "nothing succeeds like success." And this applies in our relationships with people as well as within ourselves. If people

"Now, isn't that just like a tree?"

DAY © *Saturday Evening Post*

are kind to us, we learn to have faith in their kindness, and this faith of ours in turn encourages them to act their kind-

---

* Psychological testing has demonstrated that with equal control-groups the same hard question was answered less well when it followed an impossible one than when it followed an easy one.

est toward us; while, if they are unkind to us, we tend not to have faith in them, and our suspicion in turn encourages the worst in them. "Man creates the very thing he fears" is the opposite side of the coin from the success of success. Both appear to be the social (in the sense of being concerned with many people) counterparts of the individual vicious and benign cycles.

Faith involves taking a chance. This is what the American Founding Fathers did when they granted the vote for

CLAUDE © *The New Yorker Magazine, Inc.*

the first time in history to the average man. How did they know that the pioneer in his coonskin cap, the hardbitten New England farmer, and the clipper-ship sailor, who had always been ruled by a king, would be able to judge leaders and issues and, in effect, govern themselves? They did not know: they only had faith.

Similarly, the psychiatrists who, through their treatment

of patients and their books for the general public, attempt to dethrone the old king (the unconscious policeman) and encourage the average person consciously to govern himself do not *know* what the result will be. They only have faith.

They are willing to admit that making conscious decisions is about the hardest work in the world; they are willing to admit that exercising will power and self-control is far more difficult than simply following either unconscious or outside orders. But they believe in the dignity of the individual, and therefore are willing to stake their lives (professionally speaking) on the ability of large numbers of individuals in the long run consciously to choose what is good both for themselves and for other people.

In the making of such conscious choices there will surely be mistakes—frustrating, harmful, even irrevocable mistakes. And of course we have to assume responsibility for the mistakes we make, since we do not want others to suffer in our stead. But we do not have to assume these in the sense of emotionally bearing them like an albatross around our neck for the rest of our life. Just as through insight we can help other people to stop crying over spilled milk, so, to some extent, through insight we can help ourselves.

All of us arrive at adulthood with plenty of milk having been spilled, by ourselves, by our parents (and their parents)—in effect, by all the people who ever lived and their parents. Either we remain soured by these mistakes of the past in so far as they affect our own basic urges and feelings, or we try, through understanding, to progress beyond them. Our unconscious policeman will use his billy of anxiety to try to keep us in the dark. And it will take courage to defy him. But we can do it if we mobilize our conscious knowledge and will power in the light of that flickering beam which psychiatry has focused on the workings of the deeply unconscious parts of us. In this direction inner freedom lies. Not freedom to be all-powerful, as the infant may suppose himself to be; not freedom to be all-perfect, as the adolescent may expect himself to be; but freedom to make new mistakes, perhaps more mature mistakes, in any event not forever the same old childish or irrational mistakes, repeated (like the ministrations of the compulsive handwasher) over and over again regardless of changing circumstances. And as through trial and error we perhaps learn better ways of living with ourselves and other people—and in turn perhaps our children learn even more—who knows where such a zigzagging upward spiral might lead?

Epilogue: A Final Prescription

◇◇◇

I think that, ere long, science will again become imaginative, and that, as we become more profound, we may become also more credulous.

BENJAMIN DISRAELI

ALTHOUGH PSYCHIATRY has much to offer people, it is also likely for a short time, at least, to make them overinterpret their own or others' feelings and actions. As the secretary to the psychiatrist wailed,

> *If I'm early, he thinks I'm overanxious*
> *If I'm late, he thinks I'm hostile, and*
> *If I'm on time, he thinks I'm compulsive.*

Plain horse-sense is not to be ignored, nor is the good old-fashioned hunch. If it were not for their blind hypotheses, scientists, psychiatrists included, might have no idea where to start their experiments. Similarly, if other individuals had refused to follow their intuitions, America might not have been discovered and the greatest works of art might not have been created.

[251

Just as there is room in prose and poetry for exclamation points as well as question marks, so is there room in life for living and laughing and loving without a second thought; therefore the final suggestion of the authors to the reader is to let as much of this book as seems to want to, sink in, and for the rest: ☞

Don't analyze . . . dream.

© Abner Dean

Glossary

ALTHOUGH DYNAMIC PSYCHOLOGY is one of the youngest sciences, much of its vocabulary has already found its way into our daily speech. But for some reason many of these terms have adopted new meanings in transit. Today psychological terms frequently mean one thing to the doctor and quite another to the layman. In an attempt to increase mutual understanding, we are defining here the more common of these words, together, when this is indicated, with their double meanings. (Oddly enough, lay terms like "conflict" and "adjustment," which have been adopted by the doctors, have kept their original meanings.) In compiling this glossary, we have liberally borrowed from Hinsie and Shatzky's Psychiatric Dictionary.

WORD	*What it means to* the DOCTOR	*What it means to* the LAYMAN
ambivalence	Co-existence of opposed emotions; e.g., love and hate. Damning with faint praise is an expression of ambivalence. Unconscious	A conscious wanting to do two different things at the same time; e.g., staying home and going out.

WORD	*What it means to* the DOCTOR	*What it means to* the LAYMAN
ambivalence (cont.)	emotions always have an opposite core.	
alcoholism	An abnormal state derived from excessive drinking of alcohol, usually over a long period of time. Alcoholism is a serious psychological disorder that in turn may cause a number of diseases of body and mind.	Applied loosely to people who drink more than seems good for them; common belief is that the person could snap out of it by himself if he really wanted to.
blocking	Sudden cessation of thought, feeling, or action due to strong unconscious emotional interference.	Forgetting.
character neurosis	A form of neurosis not characterized by anxious, hysterical, or obsessive-compulsive symptoms, but by a marked and undesirable deviation of character, such as continued aggression, oversensitivity, or dependency. Yet to some extent all neuroses include character neurosis.	

WORD	What it means to the DOCTOR	What it means to the LAYMAN
climacterium (adj.: *climacteric*)	Changes of the body in connection with the endocrine glands, particularly as to the capacity for procreation in women. There is a similar condition in men but not pronounced. Psychological changes may co-exist, though not necessarily.	"Change of life"—applied only to women.
compulsive	Repetitive acts caused by irresistible unconscious impulses that cannot be reconciled with the person's conscious desires. Interference with these acts, such as compulsive counting, leads to enormous anxiety.	
constitution	A confusing term; the sum total of physical and psychological characteristics determined by the inherent pattern of the organism. Science so far is hardly able to dis-	Hereditary strengths and weaknesses of body and character.

256]

WORD	*What it means to* *the* DOCTOR	*What it means to* *the* LAYMAN
constitution (cont.)	entangle the inner forces of constitution from the forces of environment.	
delusion	A false belief, usually incorrigible, due to mental illness; the conviction today that the moon is made of cheese would be a delusion while the conviction before the time of Galileo that the earth was flat was ignorance.	Any mistaken idea.
depression	Condition of feeling sad, dejected, inactive, low; may occur as part of normal or exaggerated grief and in its severest form in psychoses (see mania).	"Feeling blue"—applied usually to normal people.
dynamic	A term borrowed from physics referring to operation of hypothetical mental forces. The assumption of many such conscious and unconscious forces operating together	Lively.

WORD	What it means to the DOCTOR	What it means to the LAYMAN
dynamic (cont.)	with or against each other is one of the basic notions of modern psychiatry.	
ego	Latin word for I; in Freud's theory of personality, ego refers to the conscious and unconscious forces serving self-preservation; the unconscious part of the ego being identical with the so-called unconscious defenses. Ego reconciles the demands of reality, the id, and the superego.	Ego often used as synonymous with "pride." Also used to define the conscious self, the "I," but carrying connotations of egomaniac or egocentric.
erotic	Derived from name of Eros, Greek god of love and play. Erotic may refer to all forms of love.	"Sexually arousing," "sexy," "dirty."
fixation	Emotional development arrested at a particular level in the early life-history of the individual.	Idiosyncrasy; e.g., a fixation about untied shoelaces.
functional	An unprecise term that in medical and	With clear-cut function or pur-

WORD	*What it means to* *the* DOCTOR	*What it means to* *the* LAYMAN
functional (cont.)	psychiatric jargon is synonymous with psychological or psychogenic as against physical.	pose, as in modern architecture.
hallucination	An erroneous perception, caused by mental illness. Hearing of voices, seeing of visions are common examples.	
hysteria	A neurotic reaction in which psychological symptoms imitate other illnesses, as in hysterical blindness or paralysis.	Laughing and crying at the same time.
id	The wholly unconscious part of personality in Freud's theory which includes the instincts such as the sexual and aggressive.	
identification	An unconscious molding of oneself upon another person, the conscious counterpart being imitation.	Telling who someone is.

WORD	What it means to the DOCTOR	What it means to the LAYMAN
inhibition	An unconscious restraining of instinctual forces, which is not necessarily pathological.	Shyness.
inferiority complex	A term introduced by Alfred Adler to denote feelings of inadequacy developed during childhood when the young human being is plagued by feelings of uncertainty, dependence, and unsatisfactory function of his body.	Applied to normal people who are shy or to normal people who are compensatorily brusque or boastful.
libido (adj.: *libidinous*)	Refers to the psychic energy associated with the sexual instinct.	"Sexy," "dirty."
mania	A severe state of excitement, agitation; or a pathologically happy mood. May also be the name of a mental disorder that at times alternates with depression.	Two distinct meanings: one, a strong desire for, as a "mania" for peaches; the other, "maniac" — someone who is violently insane or drunk.

260]

WORD	What it means to the DOCTOR	What it means to the LAYMAN
megalomania	An incorrigibly high estimate of oneself based on falsifications of reality.	
morbid	Diseased.	Depressed.
negative feeling	One with destructive implications.	One of opposition.
nervous	Refers to nerves; i.e., parts of the nervous system which connect nerve cells, playing a role in perception, motor function, and higher mental processes.	Jittery.
neurosis (adj.: *neurotic*)	General term referring to behavior that is characterized by a chronic, repetitive pattern of maladjustment to the ordinary problems of living. It may take the form of anxiety, compulsions, obsessions, phobias, or hysteria. Still it is, strictly speaking, not a disease and is	"Queer," "insane," "peculiar." Often confused with psychotic and psychopathic; general belief is that if the "neurotic" really wanted to he could stop being the way he is.

WORD	What it means to the DOCTOR	What it means to the LAYMAN
neurosis (cont.)	therefore different from the severe behavioral disorders (psychoses) and the illnesses that are partly caused by emotional factors (psychosomatic illnesses).	
obsessive	Ideas or emotions that persist despite their being incompatible with the conscious part of the personality.	
Œdipus complex	Based on Greek saga of Œdipus Rex, who slew his father unknowingly and married his mother. Freud discovered that every child at the age of three to four becomes consciously or unconsciously attracted to the parent of the opposite sex and develops aggressive and jealous feelings toward the parent of the same sex.	Something that is dirty or disgusting, to be shunned in conversation. Our society until very recently demanded that children love both parents at all times and to an equal degree.

WORD	What it means to the DOCTOR	What it means to the LAYMAN
Œdipus complex (cont.)	These unconscious sexual and aggressive feelings are mostly dissolved as the child develops normally.	
organic	Refers to organs of the body; is identical in medicine and psychiatry with somatic and physical, often contrasted with functional.	Living, as against not living.
pathological	Pertaining to disease, physical and mental.	"Inborn," "unusual"—"I have a pathological dislike of redheads."
personality	A word of many meanings. Psychiatrists use it mostly in the sense of integration of habitual patterns of behavior.	Charm
phobia	A morbid fear caused by objects or situations that are normally not fear-producing, such as fear of open or closed places.	Any particularized fear.

[263

WORD	*What it means to* *the* DOCTOR	*What it means to* *the* LAYMAN
phobia (cont.)	Other phobias are exaggerated fears of objects that can be dangerous, such as snakes, or of situations, such as darkness.	
positive feeling	One with constructive implications.	A strong, powerful one.
psychiatrist	A medical specialist (M.D.) who diagnoses, treats, and investigates behavior disorders, using any or all scientific methods of treatment to help his patients.	
psychiatry	A specialty of medicine dealing with mental and emotional disorders.	These two are often thought to be interchangeable.
psychoanalysis	1. A theory of personality based on Freud's fundamental discoveries. 2. A method of scientific observation which explores unconscious determinants of behavior. 3. A method of	

WORD	*What it means to* the DOCTOR	*What it means to* the LAYMAN
psychoanalysis (cont.)	treatment (see psychoanalyst). 4. An organization of practicing psychoanalysts.	
psychoanalyst	A psychiatrist (with rare exceptions) who adheres to Freud's theories of normal and abnormal personality and treats his patients by a verbal method increasing their insight into troublesome unconscious conflicts.	
psychogenic	Caused by psychological processes, in contrast to organic processes.	
psychology	A scientific discipline exploring behavior of man and animals. As such, psychology is a basic science of psychiatry just as anatomy is a basic science of medicine. *Clinical psychology* is a sub-specialty of psychology	Motive or way of thinking, as in: "What's his psychology?"

WORD	*What it means to* the DOCTOR	*What it means to* the LAYMAN
psychology (cont.)	dealing with the development of tests to diagnose normal and abnormal behavior. Clinical psychologists are particularly equipped to help psychiatrists in research. Psychologists usually hold Ph.D., M.S., or M.A. degrees.	
psychoneurosis (adj.: *psychoneurotic*)	See neurosis.	
psychopath	An obsolete term that is replaced by the term "antisocial character." Such persons suffer from strong antisocial drives that are not checked by their conscious and unconscious forces of control. The term psychopathic, derived from "psychopathology," may be used to denote all abnormalities of behavior.	Extreme, as in "psychopathic liar," though not necessarily abnormal.

WORD	*What it means to* *the* DOCTOR	*What it means to* *the* LAYMAN
psychosis (adj.: *psychotic*)	A sweeping mental disorder, chronic or acute, which seriously impairs feelings, will power, and intelligence. It may have organic or psychological causes, or both. The common psychoses are schizophrenia, manic-depressive reactions, psychoses due to	Confused with neurosis.
	infections and toxic conditions (delirium tremens of alcoholics being one), and psychoses due to organic diseases of the brain (including the senile disorders).	
psychosomatic	This hybrid word refers to the unity of mind and body in modern medical and psychiatric theory. It also refers to a number of illnesses such as high-blood-pressure disease, asthma, ulcer of the	

WORD	What it means to the DOCTOR	What it means to the LAYMAN
psychosomatic (cont.)	stomach, some allergies, which presumably have physical as well as psychological causes. Psychosomatic research is concerned with the relationship of bodily and psychological phenomena.	
psychotherapy	Treatment of personality disorders by behavioral (mostly verbal) means—either giving the patient insight (modeled after psychoanalysis, which has more ambitious aims of remolding the total personality) or using techniques of reassurance, or manipulation of the environment, or using both approaches in a large number of variations. Some psychotherapists have effectively used hypnosis, though this approach is still large-	Confused with psychiatry and psychoanalysis.

WORD	*What it means to* the DOCTOR	*What it means to* the LAYMAN
psycotherapy (cont.)	ly in the field of exploration.	
regression	An unconscious mechanism of defense consisting of returning to an earlier, more primitive form of living. Freud compared it to the retreat of an army to previously held positions.	Going backward either consciously or unconsciously.
repression	Unconscious keeping of thoughts, drives, and emotions from the conscious mind because they would create too much anxiety or confusion.	Conscious curbing of conscious desires, as in self-control; also meek and mild, as in: "He seems like a repressed child."
resistance	The instinctual opposition to laying bare unconscious forces. Removal of unconscious resistance is a major task of psychoanalytic treatment.	Stubbornness.
Rorschach test	One of the frequently used personality tests, con-	

WORD	*What it means to* the DOCTOR	*What it means to* the LAYMAN
Rorschach test (cont.)	sisting of asking the subject to tell what a series of oddly shaped ink-blots mean to him. The patient projects his interpretations into the ink-blots; hence the test is called a projection technique. Dr. Rorschach was a Swiss psychiatrist.	
schizophrenia	A serious mental disorder, synonymous with dementia præcox, characterized by progressive loss of social contact.	
sexuality	Originally term referred to manifold activities connected with act of procreation. Since Freud's work it has been broadened considerably to include infantile sucking and many other forms of behavior originally not recognized as sexual.	Limited to sexual activity.

WORD	*What it means to the* DOCTOR	*What it means to the* LAYMAN
sublimation	A little-understood mechanism of unconscious substitution of a culturally accepted gratification for a forbidden one.	Used sneeringly, as in pointing out an old maid's love for her cat as a typical sublimation.
superego	Part of personality in Freud's theory which embodies the unconscious conscience. It is usually thought to be identical with self-punitive tendencies.	
Thematic Apperception Test (TAT)	In this test, designed by Dr. H. A. Murray at Harvard, the subject is asked to talk about a series of pictures which are presented to him. His personality is interpreted on the basis of the themes he chooses.	
trauma (adj.: *traumatic*)	Wound; psychological or physical damage.	Shocking.

Bibliography

POPULAR GENERAL TEXTS

BEACH, F. A. and FORD, C. S.: *Sexual Patterns of Behavior*. Harper; 1951.

BEERS, C.: *A Mind That Found Itself*. Doubleday; 1948, 7th ed. The book that started the Mental Hygiene Movement.

BENEDEK, T.: *Insight and Personality Adjustment*. Ronald Press; 1946. An excellent survey from the psychoanalytic viewpoint.

BERNE, E.: *The Mind in Action*. Macmillan; 1950. One of the good books of its kind.

BINGER, C.: *The Doctor's Job*. W. W. Norton; 1945. A fine presentation of the medical problem from a psychological and social viewpoint.

CAMERON, D. E.: *Life Is for Living*. Macmillan; 1948. A straightforward statement.

EIDELBERG, L.: *Take off Your Mask*. International Universities Press; 1948. An interesting presentation of an analyst's life.

FRANK, L. K.: *Nature and Human Nature*. Rutgers University Press; 1951. A scholarly discussion.

FREEMAN, L.: *Fight against Fears*. Crown; 1951. A gripping account of the author's psychoanalysis.

HUGHES, M. M., ed.: *The People in Your Life*. Knopf; 1951. Statements by ten authorities who spoke at Town Hall in New York City.

JOHNSON, W.: *People in Quandaries*. Harper; 1946. From the semantic viewpoint.

KUBIE, L. S.: *Practical and Theoretical Aspects of Psychoanalysis*. International Universities Press; 1950. The best introduction for the intelligent lay person.

LIEBMAN, J.: *Peace of Mind*. Simon and Schuster; 1946. A good book, for a long time a first best-seller.

MAY, ROLLO: *The Meaning of Anxiety*. Ronald Press; 1950.

MENNINGER, K. A.: *The Human Mind*. Knopf; 1947, 3rd ed. A detailed account of the more important mental activities from the psychoanalytic point of view.

MENNINGER, W. C. and LIEF, M.: *You and Psychiatry*. Scribner's; 1948. A good statement about the practical side of basic analytic concepts.

OVERSTREET, HARRY: *The Mature Mind*. Norton; 1949.

PRESTON, G.: *Psychiatry for the Curious*. Farrar & Rinehart; 1943. Refreshing.

SAUL, L.: *Emotional Maturity*. Lippincott; 1947. An excellent presentation but somewhat difficult.

MARRIAGE AND THE FAMILY

BECKER, H. and HILL, R. L., eds.: *Family, Marriage and Parenthood*. N.Y. Health; 1948. A good review.

LEVY, J. and MUNROE, R.: *The Happy Family*. Knopf; 1938. Excellent presentation.

WALLER, W. W.: *Family; a Dynamic Interpretation*. Dryden; 1938.

THE COMMUNITY

HOLLINGSHEAD, A. B.: *Elmtown's Youth*. John Wiley; 1949. A fine scientific treatise, fairly easy to read.

LYND, R. S.: *Middletown; a Study in American Culture*. Harcourt, Brace; 1937. A classic.

LYND, R. S.: *Middletown in Transition; a Study in Cultural Conflicts.* Harcourt, Brace; 1937.

Warner, W. L. and others: *Social Class in America.* Science Research Associates, 1949. Another basic book.

THE CHILD

I. *Development*

BETTELHEIM, BRUNO: *Love Is Not Enough.* Free Press; 1950.

DESCHWEINITZ, K.: *Growing Up.* Macmillan; 1935, 2nd ed.

FREUD, A.: *Psychoanalysis for Teachers and Parents.* Emerson Books; 1947. A wonderfully lucid presentation of the psycho-analytic view of human development.

GESELL, A., et al.: *Infant and Child in the Culture of Today.* Harper; 1946.

ISAACS, S.: *The Intellectual Growth in Young Children.* Routledge; 1933.

PIAGET, J.: *The Child's Conception of Physical Causality.* Harcourt, Brace; 1930.

RIBBLE, MARGARETHA: *The Rights of Infants.* Columbia University Press; 1944.

II. *Child Care*

ALDRICH, C. A. and ALDRICH, M. M.: *Babies Are Human Beings.* Macmillan; 1938. Good but somewhat dated.

REDL, FRITZ and WINEMAN, DAVID: *Controls from Within: Techniques for the Treatment of the Aggressive Child.* Free Press; 1952.

Spock, B.: *Commonsense Book of Child Care.* Simon & Schuster; 1941: also available as Pocket Book; Pocket Books, Inc. A most useful combination of information on physical and emotional development of small children.

WOLF, A. W. M.: *The Parents' Manual.* Simon & Schuster; 1941.

MORE TECHNICAL BOOKS ABOUT PSYCHIATRY

ALEXANDER, F.: *Fundamentals of Psychoanalysis.* Norton; 1948.

ALEXANDER, F., ed: *Studies in Psychosomatic Medicine.* Ronald Press; 1948.

CAMERON, N.: The Psychology of Behavior Disorders. Houghton Mifflin; 1947.

DEUTSCH, H.: Psychology of Women. Grune & Stratton; 1944–5, 2 vols.

DOLLARD, J. and MILLER, N.: Personality and Psychotherapy. McGraw-Hill; 1950.

ENGLISH, O. S. and PEARSON, G. J. H.: The Emotional Problems of Living. Norton; 1945.

ERIKSON, ERIK: Childhood and Society. Norton; 1950.

FENICHEL, O.: The Psychoanalytic Theory of Neurosis. Norton; 1945.

FREUD, A.: Ego and Mechanisms of Defense. Hogarth; 1937.

FREUD, S.: General Introduction to Psychoanalysis. Liveright; 1920.

FREUD, S.: Problem of Anxiety. Norton; 1936.

FREUD, S.: Outline of Psychoanalysis. Norton; 1949.

FREUD, S.: Basic Writings. Random House (Modern Library).

FROMM, E.: Escape from Freedom. Farrar & Rinehart; 1947.

FROMM-REICHMANN, F.: Principles of Intensive Psychotherapy. University of Chicago Press; 1950.

HORNEY, K.: The Neurotic Personality of Our Time. Norton; 1937.

KINSEY, A.: Sexual Behavior of the Human Male. Saunders; 1949.

MASLOW, A. M. and MITTELMAN, B.: Principles of Abnormal Psychology. Harper; 1951.

MASSERMAN, J.: Principles of Dynamic Psychiatry. Saunders; 1947.

MULLAHY, P.: Œdipus, Myth and Complex. Hermitage Press; 1948.

REIK, T.: Listening with the Third Ear. Farrar, Straus; 1949.

RUESCH, JURGEN and BATESON, GREGORY: Communication. Norton; 1951.

STRECKER, E. A. and EBAUGH, F. G.: Practical Clinical Psychiatry. Blakiston; 1943, 5th ed.

SULLIVAN, H. S.: Conceptions of Modern Psychiatry. W. A. White Psychiatric Foundation; 1947.

THOMPSON, C.: *Psychoanalysis: Evolution and Development.* Hermitage Press; 1950.

TOMPKINS, S.: *Contemporary Psychopathology.* Harvard; 1943.

WHITE, R.: *The Abnormal Personality.* Ronald Press; 1944.

WITMER, H., ed., et al.: *Teaching Psychotherapeutic Medicine.* The Commonwealth Fund; 1947.

ZILBOORG, G.: *History of Medical Psychology.* Norton; 1941.

PAMPHLETS

Mental Health Publications. Distributed by the National Association for Mental Health, 1790 Broadway, New York, N.Y.

I. *Mental Health of Adults*

Guide Posts to Mental Health. New York State Department of Mental Hygiene.

BINGHAM, J.: *"Do Cows Have Neuroses?"*

DUVALL, E.: *"Building Your Marriage."*

LAWTON, G. and STUART, M.: *"When You Grow Older."*

MENNINGER, W. C.: *"There Is Something You Can Do About Mental Health."*

MURRAY, J.: *"Normal Personality Development."*

PRATT, G. K.: *"Your Mind and You."*

THORMAN, G.: *"Toward Mental Health."*

WOLFF, H.: *"Life Situations, Emotions and Disease."*

YAHRAES, H.: *"Alcoholism Is a Sickness."*

II. *Mental Health of Children*

ALDRICH, C.: *"High Lights on the Psychology of Infancy."*

BINGHAM, J.: *"Do Babies Have Worries?"*

FRANK, L.: *"Fundamental Needs of the Child."*

SPOCK, B.: *"Avoiding Behavior Problems."*

"Your Child from 1–6." CHILDREN'S BUREAU, FSA.

"Your Child from 6–12." CHILDREN'S BUREAU, FSA.

Parent-Teacher Series. Publication of Teachers' College, Columbia University.

III. *Care of Mentally Ill*

DEUTSCH, A.: *"Recent Trends in Mental Hospital Care."*

STERN, E.: *"Mental Illness: a Guide for the Family."*

FILMS

The Feeling of Hostility. 1948. Canadian. 32 min. sound. About a girl whose childhood experiences lead to strong repressed hostility and fear of love. She turns to intellectual achievement for gratification.

This Is Robert. 1942. Vassar. 40 min. sound. The development of a "difficult" child from two through seven, showing his physical, emotional and social development.

Baby Meets His Parents. Encyclopædia Britannica. 11 min. sound. Shows the influence of environmental forces on the development of personality in the first years of life.

A Psychoneurosis with Compulsive Trends in the Making. The Life History of Mary from Birth to 7. 1947. Dr. Margaret Fries, N.Y. Infirmary. The effects of a supposedly "normal" home environment on the personality of a child who develops a neurosis.

Preface to Life. National Institute of Mental Health. 28 min. sound. The effects of four different types of parental care on the personality.

The Feeling of Rejection. Canadian. 70 min. sound. About a shy, timid girl who goes to a psychiatrist for headaches that turn out to be primarily due to repressed hostility and early feelings of rejection by her parents.

Overdependency. Canadian. 32 min. sound. A likable young man is crippled by frequent illnesses and complaints which foster his overdependence on his mother and wife. His psychiatrist helps him to see that he is perpetuating a childhood pattern.

Let There Be Light. U.S. Army. 58 min. sound. Army film on the treatment of psychoneurotic soldiers, illustrating the use of hypnosis, group psychotherapy, sodium pentothal, recreational therapy.

Shades of Gray. U.S. Army. Like *Let There Be Light,* with professional actors. Probably the best presentation of psychiatric problems.

Out of True. British. 40 min. sound. Hospital treatment of suicidal girl is shown in detail together with flashbacks of

[277

events in her past life which may have contributed to her illness. After many ups and downs she finally gets well.

Farewell to Childhood. 1952. International Film Bureau. 23 min. sound. This film portrays the difficulties and emotional conflicts of an adolescent girl and the problems she has of growing up. It particularly shows the rebellion against unreasonably interfering parents. The parents are helped to understand the girl's problems and her need for increasing freedom.

Fears of Children. International Film Bureau. 27 min. sound. Portrayal of how a mother's overwhelming fears and overprotectiveness make a young child of 5 very apprehensive. The mother is helped to deal with these problems by understanding them and successfully overcomes them.

The Lonely Night. International Film Bureau. 16 mm., 23 min. sound. This film contrasts the effects of two different family backgrounds upon the adult handling of hostility. In one case the children were permitted to feel hostility and to recognize that expressions of hostility were normal if properly handled. In the other, the child could not express her deep hostile feelings toward her father for bringing home a stepmother. She later became very much upset but is helped by a sensible and understanding psychiatric approach.

National Agencies for Mental Health

ALCOHOLICS ANONYMOUS
    114 Lexington Avenue, New York 16, N.Y.
AMERICAN ASSOCIATION FOR PUBLIC HEALTH
    1790 Broadway, New York 17, N.Y.
AMERICAN ASSOCIATION FOR RESEARCH IN NERVOUS AND MENTAL
DISEASES
    710 West 168th Street, New York 32, N.Y.
AMERICAN ASSOCIATION OF PSYCHIATRIC SOCIAL WORKERS
    1860 Broadway, New York 19, N. Y.
AMERICAN ASSOCIATION OF SOCIAL WORKERS
    1 Park Avenue, New York 16, N.Y.
AMERICAN ASSOCIATION ON MENTAL DEFICIENCY
    Mansfield Depot, Conn.
AMERICAN MEDICAL ASSOCIATION
    535 North Dearborn Street, Chicago 10, Ill.
AMERICAN NEUROLOGICAL ASSOCIATION
    710 West 168th Street, New York 32, N.Y.
AMERICAN ORTHOPSYCHIATRIC ASSOCIATION
    303 Lexington Avenue, New York 16, N.Y.
AMERICAN PSYCHIATRIC ASSOCIATION
    1785 Massachusetts Avenue, N.W., Washington 6, D.C.
AMERICAN PSYCHOANALYTIC ASSOCIATION
    245 East 82nd Street, New York 28, N.Y.
AMERICAN PSYCHOLOGICAL ASSOCIATION
    1333 16th Street, N.W., Washington 6, D.C.
AMERICAN PSYCHOSOMATIC SOCIETY
    551 Madison Avenue, New York 22, N.Y.
ASSOCIATION FOR FAMILY LIVING
    28 East Jackson Boulevard, Chicago 4, Ill.
CHILD STUDY ASSOCIATION OF AMERICA
    132 East 74th Street, New York 21, N.Y.

GROUP FOR THE ADVANCEMENT OF PSYCHIATRY
P.O. Box C, Waverley, Mass.

NATIONAL ASSOCIATION FOR MENTAL HEALTH
1790 Broadway, New York 19, N.Y.

NATIONAL COMMITTEE ON ALCOHOLISM, INC.
2 East 103rd Street, New York 29, N.Y.

NATIONAL EPILEPSY LEAGUE
Room 1916, 13 North Wells Street, Chicago 6, Ill.

NATIONAL INSTITUTE OF MENTAL HEALTH
U.S. Public Health Service (Publications and Reports Division), Bethesda 14, Md.

NATIONAL PROBATION AND PAROLE ASSOCIATION
1790 Broadway, New York 17, N.Y.

NATIONAL SOCIETY FOR CRIPPLED CHILDREN AND ADULTS, INC.
11 South LaSalle Street, Chicago 3, Ill.

U.S. CHILDREN'S BUREAU
Federal Security Agency, Washington 25, D.C.

VETERANS ADMINISTRATION
Washington 25, D.C.

A NOTE ON THE TYPE

The text of this book was set on the Linotype in ELEC-
TRA, designed by W. A. DWIGGINS. The Electra face is
a simple and readable type suitable for printing books
by present-day processes. It is not based on any historical
model, and hence does not echo any particular time or
fashion. It is without eccentricities to catch the eye and
interfere with reading—in general, its aim is to perform
the function of a good book printing-type: to be read,
and not seen.

The book was composed, printed, and bound by
KINGSPORT PRESS, Inc., Kingsport, Tennessee.